THE NEXT MASTER OF THE WORLD

KARIM MASSIMOV

THE NEXT MASTER OF THE WORLD

Artificial Intelligence

M 31   **Karim Massimov.**
       The next master of the world.
       Artificial Intelligence

— Washington DC, Amanat Publishing House, 2019. – 284 p.

ISBN-13: 978-0-578-56929-1

With the ever-increasing applications of Artificial Intelligence (AI), we are witnessing the birth of a new era, marked by the emergence of previously unknown industries and by breakthrough innovations in medicine, bioengineering, robotics, weaponry and space exploration.

The author presents a step by step, detailed overview of the key milestones as well as concepts such as the so-called "Singularity" of the futurists, while reviewing the AI technology already in our everyday lives.

Next he discusses the main features of the national AI strategies of a number of countries before concluding with an attempt to define what Kazakhstan's role might be in applying AI technologies, and indeed in participating in their further development, to participate in the new era of AI dominance.

Acknowledgments

The First President of Kazakhstan, Nursultan Nazarbayev, has played an important role in inspiring me to write this book: during his Speech to the Nation in October 2018, he dedicated a significant part of his address to the importance of Artificial Intelligence in Kazakhstan.

I wish to thank those who have read through various drafts of the manuscript and have provided valuable editorial assistance along the way: His Highness Sheikh Tahnoon bin Zayed Al Nahyan, Jacques Attali, Herman Greff, Kai-Fu Lee, Edward Luttwak, Jack Ma, Wanli Min, Rajeev Misra, Cyril Muller, Filip Relander, Masayoshi Son, Ling Shao, Arkadiy Volozh, Peng Xiao.

Special thanks to participants of the art contest "Kazakhstan of my dreams": Stanislav Anastasev, Polina Goryaeva, Veronica Morskaya, Vladimir Savitsky, Talgat Serikov, Akmaral Shaimagambetova, and Sophia Son.

Forewords

From Kazakhstan's Smart City program and its powerful economic and social impact, to the heavy investments by nations like the US, China, UAE and Singapore, the fact is that AI is here, and it is here to stay.

The fundamental question, however, is whether humans will control AI in the future, or are they creating a new deity for themselves?

Karim Massimov expertly surveys the many Gilgamesh projects related to AI out there, and he guides us to foresee the most realistic outcomes of this powerful development.

His Highness Sheikh Tahnoon bin
Zayed Al Nahyan

AI is the new electricity, and it will change the world forever.

Yet, despite its positive benefits for virtually all domains of human activity, businesses and governments across the world remain unprepared for the greatest disruption to jobs, industries and the way of life they've ever had to reckon with. Dr. Massimov's book suggests that Kazakhstan is bucking this trend, as AI's role in that society comes into focus.

The Next Master of the World is a much needed, comprehensive view of AI advancements and their impact as they are already playing out around the world.

We have a great responsibility to ensure that AI can live up to its potential as a potent force for good in society. Dr. Massimov makes an eloquent case for taking action now to get it right.

**Dr. Kai-Fu Lee,
former president of Google China, prominent investor in AI technology, and author of the book AI Superpowers: China, Silicon Valley and the New World Order**

AI opens a new chapter in the history of human-kind, finding solutions for key challenges and risks. We are living in a very interesting time, seeing the very beginning of this global shift in our history, and we can be a leading part of it. From this point of view, Dr. Massimov's book is not just an impressive and insightful work, but also a contribution to this global change.

The author extensively outlines and describes the key issues that have been overlooked and where progress lags behind the technological advancement and investment progress of AI technology. Areas such as the international legal framework, multi-national coordination and regulation are key to implementing AI, not only for the global community but also for governments.

To my pleasant surprise, Kazakhstan's leadership fully comprehends the potential of AI as a global tool of the future.

The author's in-depth analysis of trends and ever-developing AI systems, and how they are being applied to various sectors such as medicine and the military, provides the reader an opportunity to imagine what other applications AI might have in everyday life.

I see that Kazakhstan has great potential to become an AI leader and trendsetter in the post-Soviet region.

Mutual cooperation, freedom for investments and the right legal framework can only bring even greater success to AI in the world.

Masayoshi Son,
Chairman and CEO of SoftBank,
Chairman of Arm Holdings

Dr. Massimov's book begins with an experiment on digitalization in a small Kazakhstani city with a population of 13,000.

This experiment showed people that digital technology, represented by artificial intelligence, already can serve as a kind of model for comprehensive and sustainable development.

While books on artificial intelligence are being constantly published today, this volume's point of view further reveals the essence of the digital age: digital technologies are not about private benefits, but altruism; they concentrate not on empowering oneself, but on creating opportunities for others. Digital technologies should contribute not only to the success of small groups of people and countries, but also to the overall development of the remaining 80% of the world's population.

Today the world faces all kinds of problems, but achieving universal, environmentally sound, and sustainable development in places such as the small Kazakh city described in the book is a real solution.

Artificial intelligence, the internet of things, and blockchain are technologies for people. However, they are not just technologies, but also a way for us to reflect upon and rethink the world.

The superiority of artificial intelligence over humanity is not the main cause for concern. The question is whether humanity possesses sufficient wisdom. Because the future does not depend on intelligence, but on the wisdom of the people behind it.

The industrial era turned people into machines, while the digital era is turning machines into people. I believe that in the future, machines will be more like machines, and people will be more like people.

Machines cannot replace people, but can become partners for humankind. Technologies are not about leaving people unemployed, but about enabling people to do more valuable and important things.

Today, humanity is entering the digital age.

Today, humanity has never experienced the digital age.

Just as nobody could imagine landing on the moon before we had oil, people today will be unable to imagine what might be attainable in the future until we master digital data.

However, people's curiosity for the future and unlimited courage is what distinguishes them from machines.

Therefore, by opening this book, we also open a page in the future of humankind.

Jack Ma,
founder and executive chairman
of Alibaba Group

From my heart.

Kazakhstan has long been a place of change, a country home to and bordered by many different cultures. As we enter a new technological age driven by the rise of artificial intelligence, I believe it is inevitable that the rate of change facing modern societies will accelerate. Around the world, countries large and small are working hard to unlock the opportunities that will be presented by the Information Revolution—a future in which our cities, industries and social systems will look very different.

As a former Prime Minister and intelligence chief, Karim Massimov has spent decades building the infrastructure and economy that underpins Kazakhstan today. His work as a public servant was central to the development of Nur-Sultan as a dynamic, forward-thinking city, bolstered by academic institutions such as Nazarbayev University which are breaking new ground in independent research. This breadth of experience, not to mention his passion for sport, particularly triathlon, provide a unique perspective on the social identity and outlook of modern Kazakhs. In this book, Massimov presents a considered and insightful exploration of how AI can be a catalyst for Kazakhstan's future on the global stage.

Artificial intelligence is a broad family of technologies and tools with the potential to transform every existing industry and create entirely new ones. Breakthroughs and intellectual property drive the success or failure of entire industries and regions. Many of the largest industries on earth—energy, transportation, agriculture, education, healthcare—have been relatively untouched by technology. Vast progress in computing power, the accessibility of data and the intelligence of systems that can understand it is reshaping these industries for the better while unlocking economic growth. As seen in the digitalization of the country's economy, Kazakhstan has already taken critical steps towards a bold future. Accelerating this momentum through the application of AI across multiple industries will unlock Kazakhstan's potential as the technological gateway to Central Asia.

Rajeev Misra,
Board Director, Executive Vice President, Softbank Group Corp

AI today invokes an enthusiasm akin to what the Internet did twenty years ago. In the 1990's, the buzz of Internet proved a harbinger of an unprecedented technology transformation that changed how we consume the news, do our banking, or even read this book. In the subsequent two decades, we saw policymakers struggle to regulate the ever-changing global Internet platform, which invited billions of people to rapidly exchange ideas, goods and services.

Unprecedented wealth was created, but concentrated primarily in the behemoth companies of the developed nations. Unsurprisingly, a digital divide formed between those nations who embraced the Internet and charged ahead, and those who did not. By the early 2010's, this digital divide had morphed into a very apparent economic chasm around the world.

Dr. Massimov understands this, and he knows AI has exponentially more potential than the Internet to change the world. As the former Prime Minister of Kazakhstan with a unique insight into the country's economy and foreign relations, Dr. Massimov is excellently positioned to discuss AI from an international perspective and place Kazakhstan within AI's global narrative. His foresight guides the nation in its fundamental need to stand on the right side of the upcoming AI divide. Powerfully captured in this book is an impetus for change.

In recent years, Kazakhstan has made impressive strides in their digitalization and preparation for AI. As Dr. Massimov notes, the country's online government portal already has half of the population as registered users. 80% of the homes are connected to the Internet, with Nur-Sultan, Almaty, and Shymkent implementing 5G connectivity by the end of 2019.

Smart cities are being built, transport logistics are being optimized, and the oil and gas sector is being streamlined. Within 15 years, Dr. Massimov predicts an impressive 40% increase in Kazakhstan's private sector revenues directly resulting from the nation's adoption of AI.

The United Arab Emirates, a close friend to Kazakhstan, is exemplified in the book as a pioneer in AI implementation and innovation. In 2017, the UAE launched a national AI strategy and became the first country to create a Ministry of Artificial Intelligence. The geopolitical realities and environmental challenges in the region call for AI solutions that extend to a broad range of sectors, many of which are applicable to Kazakhstan. As evidenced in the book, the Kazakh leadership keenly recognizes their opportunity to execute a superior national AI strategy by working with the global champions.

This book is not an exercise in scientific exploration. It is an actionable and impactful survey of the current AI landscape written by a statesman who stands to bring his country forward in the profound AI race. A fresh perspective from a wise leader, this book is a most welcomed one in the growingly echoing collection of literature on AI.

Peng Xiao,
CEO Pegasus FZ LLC

The key idea

"What makes ... projects fantastic are the
enormous prospects that will open up if
a successful solution is found..."

Georgy Flyorov, April 1942

In December 2018, Kazakhstan's first president, Nursultan Nazarbayev, toured "Smart Aqkol," Kazakhstan's first smart city pilot project, which was established in a small local administrative center of some 13,000 residents.

Aqkol was completely digitized using smart video monitoring systems, automated energy-use controls and pollution monitoring. The entire town was served by a high-speed internet network, and a multi-layered digital map was created with information not only about buildings, structures and land, but also about utility and infrastructure networks. All the data is integrated at a single situation center, which also receives information from all public buildings, schools, hospitals and government agencies.

Thus, a complete database was created and updated in real time to provide solutions based on data analysis and to alert monitors to any abnormalities. However, the main idea was not to pursue technological solutions but rather economic benefits and the improved wellbeing of local residents. Within a few months after the pilot was implemented, public safety improved, residents' utilities bills decreased significantly and they no longer needed to visit government agencies and collect paperwork.

The pilot project demonstrated that a "smart city" is not just a futuristic concept, but an integral infrastructure of artificial intelligence (AI), which collects data from sensors, video cameras, and satellite images and can ensure the efficient and indeed optimal management of the administrative center.

I firmly believe that this experiment should be extended to all of the 17 larger cities and more than 200 towns of our country. This would be most useful for the well-being of all Kazakhstanis, and an exemplary way of using artificial intelligence systems! But AI offers much greater opportunities than just the creation of smart cities.

By now the term is widely known, but vast misunderstandings persist about actual phenomena and concepts in the world of AI. Popular culture is replete with images of crazy cyborgs and robot uprisings, among other scare stories imagined by fiction writers. There are also more realistic concerns, about human employment, for example, that start from reasonable assumptions but are then greatly exaggerated.

Artificial intelligence refers to the ability of machines to think rationally, and make decisions in human fashion (Wooldridge, 2018) through what is now called "machine learning" and "deep learning." For example, supermarket managers can use AI to plan the purchases of goods (by regression), a bank can use it to evaluate the creditworthiness of borrowers (by classification), and Netflix can recommend other movies you might want to watch (by clustering)—these are all examples of machine learning.

Deep learning combines all machine learning methods with extremely large data sets, now described by the term "big data."[1]

The first, second, and third industrial revolutions created new general-purpose technologies that radically changed the way certain very basic problems were solved, such as mass production, transportation, and communications, which led to overall productivity growth and innovation. The first industrial revolution was centered on the steam engine, which led to the development of the coal, metallurgical and steel industries, as well as the construction of railways and canals. The second industrial revolution was marked by the invention of electricity, which was followed by the development of telecommunications and the rise of the global oil and gas industry. It brought the telegraph, telephones, cars and aircraft into our lives. Finally, the information technologies of the third industrial revolution reformatted our way of life by introducing computers, the internet, and the automation of many work processes.

It is impossible today to imagine our life without electricity, cars or the internet. But what about tomorrow? The Gartner company predicts that in the next five years we will see the widespread introduction of 5G networks and virtual assistants (Panetta, 2018). Trends over the next ten years include quantum computing, smart robots, biochips, and smart cities. In the period after that, artificial general intelligence, exoskeletons, 4D-printers, flying autonomous vehicles and biohacking will appear.

In general, the future of artificial intelligence promises three main trends for humanity.

First is the dawning of a new era of supernations led by the United States and China. Some experts even talk about a new cold war and compare the potential of artificial intelligence (especially in the military sphere) with the atomic bomb. The two countries have already been drawn into a fierce competition.

For example, on May 16, 2019, the US Department of Commerce blacklisted the Chinese company Huawei, prohibiting it from buying American equipment for any future projects ("SShA vnesli," 2019).

This simple example served as a clear signal for other countries: you need to hurry. The countdown is not in years, but in months.

The second trend is a shift in influence away from natural-resources and financial corporations to technology giants, the supercorporations. In the words of Anand Giridharadas, author of the book Winners Take All, we see the emergence of the so-called "new feudal elite from Silicon Valley" (Giridharadas, 2018).

For example, Huawei is a leader in the technology of new-generation 5G communications. Operating systems and search engines, as well as a great deal of hardware and software, are largely owned by the Alphabet, Microsoft, IBM and Apple corporations. In the field of autonomous vehicles and the space industry the leaders are Alphabet's Google (again), along with Tesla and SpaceX. Corporations like Facebook and Tencent shape market trends in social media and messaging applications. Amazon, eBay and the Alibaba Group dominate retail and wholesale online trading.

The rapid growth of supercorporations demonstrates another important aspect of the new realities of competition. The fight for resources is a thing of the past. The main struggle today is for big data generated by people.

The third, more distant trend points to the famous Gilgamesh project. If it is implemented, a new biological caste of superhumans will appear on Earth. Obviously, this will only be possible due to the relentless progress of artificial intelligence.

In this context, the key trend predicted by futurists and well-known investors such as Ray Kurzweil and Masayoshi Son is the advent of a new era of "singularity," i.e., the coming of a future in which technologies will change so much that they will become incomprehensible to humans. Some speculate that this could happen by 2050.

But the outlines of such a future are already visible today. This is the main message of this book. While this is not a scientific treatise, it is not fiction, either. This book describes how artificial intelligence is beginning to reformat our world, its socio-economic structure, markets, and political systems, and is beginning to influence our personal choices.

Today the practical applications of AI are already present in a wide range of industries, from finance to medical image processing and fraud detection. Artificial intelligence is beginning to replace important elements of the existing professions, while expanding possibilities in broad fields of activity, notably medicine, law and commerce in general.

For example, in the field of medicine, artificial intelligence can already analyze not only MRI and CT imaging data, but also sensory data, for the diagnosis, treatment and monitoring of a growing number of diseases.

In the world of business, the ability of AI to analyze data and predict outcomes can give a huge advantage to AI-using companies. Any computation and classification task can now be automated by using artificial intelligence, to obtain results in less than a second instead of days or weeks. Artificial intelligence also has a huge potential for the drastic modernization of the extractive industries, especially in the energy sector.

These technological, ethical and philosophical phenomena are visibly transforming the entire financial sector: basic financial services are being automated with the help of robotic consultants, while AI methods are being successfully used to detect fraud, and assess and manage risks.

The transport sector is also being transformed by the introduction of systemic AI applications. For example, the key to a successful transition to autonomous vehicles is the implementation of AI infrastructures, most notably smart cities, in which vehicles could move autonomously far earlier, and far more reliably, than in our present cities.

Not surprisingly, the artificial intelligence market is growing very rapidly: recent estimates indicate that AI applications could generate as much as $15 trillion globally by 2030.

There is, of course, another side to all this: artificial intelligence is also changing political processes and, importantly, electoral processes. We all know the examples of the Brexit vote and the 2016 US elections. The entire world is discussing those two events, because they put at the forefront another, more important, question about how the world around us is changing because of AI technologies in ways to which state institutions can only adapt slowly and imperfectly.

All in all, AI achievements so far are both extremely positive and very complex, in ways illustrated in the "Red List" chapter in this book.

Further, in the "Supernations" chapter, some current strategies for the development of artificial intelligence are analyzed. Today more than thirty national AI strategies are known. All pursue two goals above all: to adapt to the challenges posed by the AI transformation, and to obtain its promised economic benefits. Of course, the two main examples in the book are the national strategies of the United States and China. But for a developing country like Kazakhstan, the example of other states, such as the United Arab Emirates and Singapore, is also important. Those latter two have become pioneers in the construction of national platforms for artificial intelligence.

The question is whether the world can cope with future changes and join forces to do so (see the chapter "Flyorov and Einstein").

The chapter entitled "Supercorporations" talks about the growing influence and capabilities of big technology companies, primarily from the United States and China. It is hard to imagine the modern world without the products and services of Alibaba, Amazon, Apple, Facebook, Google, Huawei, IBM, Microsoft, Nvidia and more. The founders of these technology giants continue to dominate not only the list of the richest people on the planet, but also the attention of the world.

It is important for Kazakhstan to build partnerships not only with the major technology giants, but also with start-ups and venture funds, in order to build our own capacity in this area.

This study aims to provide a comprehensive look at the phenomenon of AI. For example, the chapter on Project Gilgamesh presents evidence that life extension through the improvement of physical and intellectual abilities is no longer science fiction, but rather a real likelihood in the not-so-distant future.

Such developments naturally raise the question of the legal regulation of artificial intelligence (see the chapter "Asilomar Principles") and its political limitation.

The book concludes with a reflection on the role and place of Kazakhstan in the new world shaped by the imminent dominance of artificial intelligence applications. An analysis of the current situation in Kazakhstan and the state of digitalization in the country is followed by a review of prerequisites for developing the country's own AI potential, and of the opportunities to implement a national AI strategy.

AI systems are advancing rapidly—indeed, so fast that in a year or two our country could be left behind as a "forever outsider" in the global AI race. To prevent such a scenario (see the chapter "Kazakhstan"), we need to implement our own strategy, and create the most favorable legal environment possible for interactions with all foreign jurisdictions, including technology companies and researchers from Europe, Japan, the US, China and other countries.

At the same time, the protection of citizens' personal rights cannot be jeopardized. And along with changes to legislation, an innovative modernization of the entire infrastructure will be required, which will generate the maximum possible amount of data necessary for the development of artificial intelligence.

We need to understand that humanity is taking its first steps in actually applying AI applications and systems. Extreme, even fatal scenarios are not impossible, but they are improbable. We cannot use them as an excuse to hinder progress and do nothing in the present.

We truly must understand and remember that the future global dominance of AI begins today.

How it all started

Key milestones in Artificial Intelligence

"The thought of making a 'thinking' machine could be exciting, controversial, and also intimidating."

From "The History of Artificial Intelligence," 2006

Artificial intelligence has been researched for decades, yet remains one of the most unexplored fields in computer science (Tate, 2014).

In the first half of the last century, science fiction introduced the world to the concept of intellectual robots. It all started with Karel Čapek's science-fiction play Rossum's Universal Robots (1920) and the "heartless" Tin Man in The Wizard of Oz (1939). The idea was further developed in the movie Metropolis (1927)[2] in which a human-like robot pretended to be a human being. In 1929 a Japanese professor, Makoto Nishimura, constructed Gakutensoku, the first real robot.

By the 1950s, a generation of scientists, mathematicians and philosophers was beginning to develop the concept of artificial intelligence, essentially launching the AI era. In the 1940s, the first digital (but not programmable) computer, the Atanasoff Berry Computer (ABC), was built. In 1945, in his seminal essay "As We May Think," Vannevar Bush[3] predicted the advent of the computer age. Five years later, in 1950, Alan Turing[4] published his paper "Computing Machinery and Intelligence," suggesting that machines could simulate human behavior and perform logic operations, such as playing chess.

At that time, Turing made the bold prediction that in about 50 years computers would be able to imitate human conversation so well that a person with average abilities would not be able distinguish whether his interlocutor was a person or a machine (Turing, 1950).

John McCarthy[5] first coined the term "Artificial Intelligence" in 1956 when he invited a group of researchers to a summer workshop called the Dartmouth Summer Research Project on Artificial Intelligence (the Dartmouth workshop, or DSRPAI). The researchers came together to clarify and develop the concepts around "thinking machines." McCarthy is said to have picked the name "artificial intelligence" for its neutrality. As the proposal for the conference put it, "The study is to proceed on the basis of the conjecture that every aspect of learning or any other feature of intelligence can in principle be so precisely described that a machine can be made to simulate it" (Marr, 2018a).

Dictionaries define AI as a field of computer science centered on machines that can imitate human intelligence, or can be human-like themselves, or even try to become human. The Oxford English Dictionary gives this definition: "The theory and development of computer systems able to perform tasks normally requiring human intelligence, such as visual perception, speech recognition, decision-making, and translation between languages." Merriam-Webster defines artificial intelligence as a branch of computer science dealing with the simulation of intelligent behavior in computers or as the capability of a machine to imitate intelligent human behavior (Marr, 2018a).

The catalyst that started AI as a research discipline was the first artificial intelligence program, the "Logic Theorist," introduced by U.S. scientists Herbert Simon, J. Cliff Shaw and Allen Newell at the Dartmouth workshop in 1956 (Moor, 2006). The "Logic Theorist" was engineered to emulate the problem-solving skills of human beings. This research was funded by the RAND Corporation.[6]

AI pioneer Arthur Samuel coined the term "machine learning" when he started thinking about programming a computer that could play chess better than the person who wrote the program. In 1958, Herbert Simon,[7] who later received the Nobel Prize in economics, predicted that a computer would become a world chess champion within ten years (Campbell, 2002). However, it took 40 years before IBM's Deep Blue famously beat former world chess champion Garry Kasparov in a six-game match in 1997.

The delay in Simon's prediction coming true was partly due to the need to create a computer powerful enough to manage the game's combinatorial complexity. Deep Blue, for instance, had 480 processors able to average about 100 million positions per second. Deep Blue's chess triumph marked a historic moment in AI's practical development. Since then, however, computer-based practice for chess masters has become routine.

In 1966, one of the first chatbots, a language processing program called ELIZA,[8] was created, followed in 1972 by a more advanced program, PARRY,[9] with an embodied conversational strategy. These innovations promised a bright future for the interpretation of conversational speech. Leading researchers from the Dartmouth workshop actively promoted their work, which helped convince the US government, in particular the Defense Advanced Research Projects Agency of the US Department of Defense (DARPA),[10] to fund artificial intelligence research. The government was particularly interested in AI's capabilities in speech recognition and high bandwidth data processing.

By 1974, computers were able to store more information and process it faster. At the same time, they became cheaper and more accessible. Because of improved machine learning algorithms, they began to reprogram themselves based on their own experience.

A new stage of AI development began in the 1980s. In particular, the Japanese government started a project to create the Fifth Generation Computer System (FGCS) that could perform more difficult tasks ("Japan," 1984). While previous computer generations had focused on increasing the number of logic elements in a single central processing unit (CPU) to perform computing tasks exclusively, Japanese scientists hoped to design computers with new capabilities. Because of the high commercial potential of such computers, there were concerns about Japan dominating this market in the same way it earlier began dominating the computer chip market. But the project was unsuccessful: by 1992, the Japanese government had spent over $850 million on the project without achieving any breakthroughs in key technological areas (Pan, 2016). Eventually, the funding for FGCS dried up and artificial intelligence dropped out of the public eye for a time.

This setback had a silver lining because it propagated the idea that AI development should be based on innovation and advanced software development. In 1997, Dragon Systems released NaturallySpeaking, the first universal program for continuous speech recognition (Shahi, 2009). It was much cheaper than previous programs and it gave access to computer speech recognition to a much wider range of users. Two months later, IBM released its competitive voice recognition software ViaVoice (Munro, 1998).

By the end of the 1990s, AI research was integrated with robotics and human-machine interfaces. Scientists started to talk seriously about artificial intelligence "agents" equipped with sentiments and able to express emotions. This gave rise to a new research field called "affective computing," aimed at analyzing human emotional responses that can be then simulated by machines. It also helped to improve dialog systems (chatbots).

In 1999, a postdoctoral associate at Massachusetts Institute of Technology built a sociable robot, called Kismet, capable of recognizing and imitating human emotions (Overby, 2017). In the same year, the Sony Corporation introduced AIBO, a robotic dog designed to "learn" from interacting with its environment. The robot's design was gradually improved to the point where the robotic pet could interact with its owner and recognize and respond to over 100 spoken commands. In 2000, Honda introduced ASIMO, a humanoid AI robot.

Another breakthrough came in the mid-2000s when Nvidia introduced its new graphics processing unit. For the first time, computers were powerful enough to process large datasets and build complex neural network architecture for a wide range of practical applications. This marked the beginning of the accelerated use of deep learning.

The term "machine reading" was first introduced in 2006 to describe the automatic comprehension of text. A year later Stanford University researchers put together ImageNet, an annotated database for visual object recognition. These innovations helped to implement such technologies as computer vision, speech recognition and machine translation.

Since 2010, technological advances in hardware and software have been paving the way for the daily use of artificial intelligence. Powerful processors and video cards in computers, smartphones and tablets have allowed a wide range of users to have constant access to AI programs. For example, Microsoft launched Kinect for Xbox 360, the first gaming device to provide body motion capture with a 3D camera and an infrared sensor.

In 2011, Apple introduced its voice assistant, Siri. In 2014, Microsoft launched Cortana, and in 2015, Amazon followed with Amazon Echo and its voice service, Alexa. These virtual assistants used a natural language interface to watch, respond and draw conclusions, and make recommendations to their users.

The assistants turned out to be impressively smart. In 2011, the computer program Watson competed in a US television quiz show in the form of an animated on-screen symbol and won against the human players. In doing so, Watson proved that it could understand natural language and was able to answer difficult questions quickly ("History of Artificial Intelligence," 2018).

In 2012, Google researchers trained a large neural network of 16,000 processors to recognize images of cats, showing it 10 million unlabeled images from YouTube videos. In 2016, Google DeepMind's AlphaGo defeated Lee Sedol, one of the world's best professional Go players, with a score of 4 to 1 (Borowiec, 2016). Before that match, it was believed that no single computer product was able to beat such an accomplished grandmaster. And yet it happened. The victory confirmed once again the superiority of artificial intelligence over people.

In 2018 IBM organized a live debate between a human debater and its AI system called Project Debater. Both sides had only 15 minutes to prepare for the topic. The machine not only carefully listened to the human expert's arguments but also responded convincingly with its own on such diverse news topics as telemedicine and subsidies for space programs. In another important step in the journey to teach AI to master the human language and mind, the AI-powered Project Debater was able to cite sources and even make a couple of jokes based on previous statements ("Think," 2019).

At a 2018 conference, Google demonstrated how Google Duplex could call an office and schedule an appointment on your behalf. The people on the other end of the line did not even realize that they were talking to a robot (Leviathan, 2018).

Finally, a few words about robotics. Boston Dynamics[11] robots (SpotMini, Handle and Atlas) have learned to run, jump, backflip and even do parkour. Humanoid robots Sophia and Han (Hanson Robotics)[12] not only look human but are also able to have a conversation and understand emotions. By interacting with each other via cloud-based storage, they constantly self-improve and learn new skills.

Some might think that these robots are silly machines incapable of multitasking, which still remains a human prerogative. After all, we designed them and not the other way around. However, human capabilities have remained limited while artificial intelligence is constantly progressing. It will surpass us sooner or later; it's only a question of time.

What is the mechanism behind AI's limitless capabilities? When machines match human intelligence we will have an era of Artificial General Intelligence, in which AI will be able to reproduce human intuitive ability in problem solving and become capable of scientific discovery. The machines of the future will be able to remember all data ever entered and every pattern ever set. Added to this will be their ability to quickly process large amounts of information. By eternally remembering vast amounts of data, machines will be able to identify patterns and draw conclusions in ways that are not available to most ordinary people. The general AI will be sufficiently autonomous to independently respond to problems arising in the environment.

Ultimately, the era will come when artificial intelligence will significantly exceed our own, and it will learn to improve itself, expanding opportunities exponentially. According to SoftBank CEO Masayoshi Son, this new era of intelligent machines that surpass people in terms of quantity and cognitive abilities will come before 2047 (Shead, 2018).

The Singularity and Ray Kurzweil's predictions

"It is a point where our models must be discarded and a new reality rules. As we move closer and closer to this point, it will loom vaster and vaster over human affairs till the notion becomes a commonplace. Yet when it finally happens it may still be a great surprise and a greater unknown."

from "The Coming Technological Singularity: How to Survive in the Post-Human Era," by Vernor Vinge (1993)

Author and scientist Vernor Steffen Vinge's concept of the "Singularity" predicts that through self-learning, artificial intelligence will one day surpass human intelligence, to the point of being incomprehensible to humans. Everyone involved with AI one way or another seems to believe that the singularity is inevitable. It's only a question of when! The onset of the singularity will be the culmination of the scientific revolution and may happen this century.

The human brain has a number of interesting properties. It is estimated to contain about one hundred billion neural cells and can perform 200 trillion operations per second. Or it might be even faster. According to Raj Reddy, professor of computer science and robotics at Carnegie Mellon University,[13] in such domains as vision, speech and motor processes, "it is more powerful than 1,000 supercomputers; however, for simple tasks such as multiplication, it is less powerful than a four-bit microprocessor" (Reddy, 1996). Processing events occurring in the human brain does not require a lot of conscious effort by humans, but they are very difficult for machines to imitate.

A massive breakthrough in understanding the mysteries of the human brain has been predicted for the near-term future. Many of the algorithms of our mind will be decoded and included in neural networks. As a result, non-biological intellects will become billions of times more powerful than the biological kind, and the Earth will become one giant computer. However, this will not happen for a long time; despite the significant progress in neurosciences, after 40 years we are still using simplistic models in neural networks.

We are unable to comprehend what will happen with the advent of the Singularity. But the hypothesis assumes that the creation of artificial super-intelligence will lead to uncontrollable technological growth, resulting in unfathomable changes to human civilization.

Well-known futurist and inventor Ray Kurzweil, who is sometimes called the "father of artificial intelligence," and famous German scientist and artificial intelligence expert Jurgen Schmidhuber,[14] believe that the Singularity will occur by approximately 2045. Computer scientist Patrick Winston[15] predicts the Singularity by 2040 while technologist and inventor Louis Rosenberg[16] thinks it will happen by 2030. According to him, it will have "its own values, its own morals, its own self-interests" (Rosenberg, 2017).

In his book The Singularity is Near: When Humans Transcend Biology, Ray Kurzweil offers some intriguing thoughts about the future (Kurzweil, 2005a). For example, he talks about sub-micro agents called nanobots, which will be injected into our bloodstreams to monitor and maintain chemical and biological balances. Other agents will specialize in patrolling the brain. They will be able to upload every stored neural pattern and synapse from the brain's cells into a supercomputer.

They would recreate the full version of the human mind's "software," including memory, emotions, instincts, thoughts and intuition. This program, like other software, will be portable to other machines. It will then think and act just like you do, but it will be immortal.

Besides being the author of a visionary book, Kurzweil is also the co-founder and chancellor of Singularity University and director of engineering at Google. He has made 147 predictions since the 1990s and has a success rate of 86% (Basulto, 2012). His successes include predicting, in 1990, that a computer would defeat a world chess champion by 1998 (Diamandis, 2015). He also predicted that computers would have wireless access to data, a prediction realized in our everyday life as Wi-Fi.

Also, Kurzweil quite accurately predicted the future ability of computers to understand human voice commands. By now, people are accustomed to using virtual assistants and sometimes talk to them as if they were living beings. It is no secret that many computer and smartphone users first consult with voice assistants before going to doctors, car mechanics or lawyers. By default, most digital assistants have pleasant female voices, which users can change. The relationship is often so close that many people call Siri, Alexa or Cortana "she" instead of "it." Soon we will have no keyboards at all and will not have to press keys with symbols on them.

His predictions about augmented and virtual reality also came true. One of the dominant leaders in this field is Microsoft. The company introduced a mixed-reality headset called HoloLens, which is used to display designer clothing and shoes or to demonstrate new automobile features. HoloLens can also help surgeons perform surgeries.

It is amazing that what Kurzweil foresaw back in the 1990s, and seemed impossible at the time, is already with us and working well. For that reason, the predictions for the next 25 years are particularly interesting. He focuses a lot of attention on 3D printing. He believes that we will be able to print our own clothing, create food very inexpensively and construct buildings in a couple of days. But the most important thing, he believes, is that we will be able to grow new tissues, and complete organs.

We are tantalizingly close to making this a reality. We just need to go past the experimental stage to widespread practical applications. Recently, a demo building was constructed using small 3D-printed Lego-style modular parts. An entire 3D-printed heart made from human cells was created as well.

If to speak about the internal use of nanorobots for medical purposes, he thinks that as early as 2032, they will be able to deliver nutrients directly to human cells and remove toxins on the way out. In another ten years, nanorobots will improve our immune system and "cleanse" our bodies of all diseases, paving the way for the idea of immortality (Kurzweil, 2005b).

By about 2030, self-driving cars will fill the roads, and people will not be allowed to drive a car not equipped with computer assistance. Driverless cars will eliminate 99% of accidents and prevent up to 2 million deaths from crashes annually.[17] By 2030 solar energy will become so cheap and widespread that it will satisfy the total energy demand of the entire human race (Kurzweil, 2005a).

Recently, at an international artificial intelligence conference,[18] Kurzweil said that based on his more than fifty years of research, data collection and analysis, he thought that the future will be much better than the present, despite what people may believe. And this is because of the outstanding achievements of human civilization, such as the significant decline of poverty worldwide, improved literacy rates and total expenditures on education, increased life expectancy, electricity in homes around the world and the number of households with computers. He says that all this makes him optimistic about the future.

Red list

"You're familiar with the phrase "Man's reach exceeds his grasp"? It's a lie. Man's grasp exceeds his nerve."

Nikola Tesla

Healthcare 2.0

The expectation of momentous changes caused by the development of artificial intelligence is fully justified by the innovative advances that have already altered the face of entire industries. Particular successes have been achieved in medicine.

Israeli researchers printed the world's first 3D heart made from human tissue. The findings of their study were published in April in *Advanced Science* (Noor, 2019). It is just a first step, but it could drastically change transplantology in the near future. Just imagine: no more compatibility or rejection issues and no more looking for a suitable donor!

Such advances have become possible in large part because of improved medical equipment, and this process keeps generating more data each year. As the trend continues, so does the potential for AI applications in medicine. Such tools as machine learning, neural networks, natural language processing and computer vision are helping AI make significant progress in learning about medicine and diagnostics.

AI improvements in healthcare promise to minimize fatal outcomes due to medical error. In the United States, for example, medical errors are the third-leading cause of death (250,000 people each year) after heart disease and cancer (Sipherd, 2018). Robot-assisted surgery has led to a five-fold reduction in surgical complications, and reduces the average hospitalization time by 21% (Schroerlucke, 2017).

The cloud-based analytical platform iQueue by LeanTaas offers operating room capacity management. Gauss Surgical's advanced AI system Triton offers monitoring for blood loss during surgery, helping in transfusion decision-making and predicting post-surgery blood hemoglobin levels. Robotic AI-powered surgery has successfully debuted in eye, heart and blood vessel surgeries and is actively expanding to other types of minimally invasive surgeries.

Artificial intelligence is helping solve an even more serious problem than medical error: out-of-hospital cardiac arrest. In 2017, in the United States and Europe alone, more than 600,000 people suffered cardiac arrest outside a hospital (Blomberg, 2019). A breakthrough came in early 2018 when, based on the processing and analysis of thousands of emergency calls to the Emergency Medical Center in Copenhagen, a special machine learning algorithm for detecting heart failure was created. This algorithm, developed by the Danish company Corti, produced more accurate results than a human doctor: 95% versus 73% (Peters, 2018). At the same time, for such an acute and transient condition, it is extremely important to quickly process information coming from the patient, which AI can do 30 seconds quicker. Often these seconds mean the difference between life and death.

Experimental studies have been conducted in other countries with similar results, and Corti's framework has now been implemented in many emergency dispatch centers around the world. Together with medical dispatchers, the machine learning framework listens to people's statements, analyses the words they use, their intonation and the background noise. If cardiac arrest is detected the system sends an immediate signal to dispatchers.

So far we only have a few example of AI surpassing diagnostics done by humans. But recent advances in image recognition and analysis have helped to reduce the time needed for processing MRI images by a factor of 1000. And it is not just primitive analysis. Arterys,[19] for example, is a solution that provides fast and accurate ventricular volume measurements. It can generate a 3D map calculating blood flow through the heart and stress in different parts of that organ (Molteni, 2017).

Israeli software company Viz-AI uses AI in a similar way to detect problems with cerebral circulation and diagnose stroke using CT brain imaging to identify problems with cerebral circulation.[20] Diagnosing a stroke is not a complicated procedure, but analyzing images one by one takes a lot of time, which increases the chances of the patient's death. This is where artificial intelligence has proven itself to be useful, accurately detecting the source of circulation problems so that doctors can act without losing any precious time.

It has to be said that the developers of imaging analysis platforms are aware of how important and urgent this diagnostics stage is. They store their innovations in the cloud, allowing global access to anybody who needs it. A notable example in this context is Zebra AI1, a service of the Israeli company Zebra Medical Vision[21] which uses unique AI algorithms to examine virtually any medical scans as cheaply as for one dollar online. When the system was tested using scans from the Oxford University hospital, it had almost a 100% success rate in identifying patients with a disease (Dent, 2017). Another leader in this field is US-based PAIGE.AI,[22] which has access to an archive of 25 million patient tissue slides and its own cancer diagnostics and treatment platform.

Much progress has also been achieved in using AI to analyze MRI and CT scans to detect breast, skin and lung cancer as well as liver lesions (see, respectively, Johnson, 2019; Mammoser, 2018; "Arterys," 2018). One of the breakthrough technologies is Butterfly IQ,[23] an ultrasound machine available for $2,000, a fifth the price of similar devices. The size of an electric razor, Butterfly IQ can scan the entire body and immediately send the image to an iPhone or iPad through an app. Built-in artificial intelligence can help detect a problem in seconds.

Quick scan analysis in real time is now being used in surgeries. Until recently it was impossible, because a surgeon cannot pause a few hours in the middle of an operation to look at some scans. Now AI can do it. Another example is IDx-DR,[24] a leading diagnostics system for detecting the first signs of diabetic retinopathy, a serious complication of diabetes mellitus that can lead to blindness. This is a very timely development, given the fact that diabetes mellitus is becoming one of the most widespread diseases of our time. According to the World Health Organization, it affects about 8.5% of all adults in the world (WHO, 2016). Of these, about 12% experience serious visual impairment, including complete loss of vision.[25] A timely exam could help detect the onset of retinopathy and prevent possible vision damage. This is exactly what the IDx-DR device is doing: detecting the early signs of the disease completely independently, without the participation of human specialists.

Artificial intelligence techniques have been very successful in predicting complications related to such serious conditions as Parkinson's disease, pulmonary arterial hypertension, cancer, diabetes and heart disease. The companies Medopad and Tencent, among others, are involved in this research. Their goal is to serve all patients who require regular health monitoring and complex treatment.

Clinical testing can often be expensive and the need to travel to a specialized center for a small but very important test can also affect a patient's health negatively. A joint Medopad-Tencent project is now creating a unique platform that allows doctors to perform such tasks as clinical monitoring of their patients remotely, including tracking of activity levels and vital signs, patient compliance, more effective scheduling of face-to-face appointments, surveys and patient training. And Medopad is expanding its collaboration with UK government organizations, giving them the opportunity to engage the population in taking better care of themselves, which inevitably increases the overall level of national wellbeing.

Another promising field for AI use in healthcare is in pharmacology, with such drug companies as Deep Genomics, Owkin, Insitro and many others leading the way. A leader among them is Atomwise,[26] a company that has developed proprietary AI technology for structure-based, small-molecule drug discovery.

Using the same statistical approach as AI technology that recognizes faces in a crowd and will enable self-driving cars, Atomwise extracts information from millions of experimental studies of protein structures. In this case AI helps analyze not thousands, like in traditional drug discovery, but billions of compounds to predict the most efficient and safe candidate for binding the target protein. The company supports researchers all over the world and has already achieved significant success in testing treatments for multiple sclerosis and the Ebola virus.

Researchers from the University of Heidelberg and Stanford University designed an AI diagnostic system based on natural images. The system has already learned to analyze various skin lesions and detect skin cancer more accurately than doctors (Agence France Presse, 2018). Other AI applications analyze data from heart rate sensors, with 85% accuracy at detecting early signs of diabetes. If their cost can be reduced, such devices could help more than 400 million people in the world suffering from this condition (Ballinger et al., 2018).

IAPB Vision experts estimate that 253 million people worldwide have moderate or severe visual impairment or are blind. 90% of them live in developing countries,[27] and the inability to see is their main obstacle to finding employment. In the US, about 70% of visually impaired adults of working age are working only part-time.[28] AI is capable of improving the quality of life for people with visual impairment by providing, for example, navigation assistance via a smartphone.

AI's computer vision capabilities could also be potentially beneficial. They could help with object recognition and reading printed text. One such mobile app is Microsoft's Seeing AI. It is offered for free and is available to users in 70 countries. Reviews of the app demonstrate the high everyday demand for it (Kelley, 2019).

Similar solutions have been implemented in OrCam MyEye, a mini-camera which, when mounted on regular eyeglasses, can verbalize what it sees (McKinsey, 2018a). The device is portable and doesn't require a smartphone but comes with a hefty price tag of about $3,000. It's clear, though, that as description technologies develop, an ever more detailed world of surrounding colors, images and faces will be available to people with visual impairments.

AI has shown a good deal of promise in cancer diagnostics and treatment. One in every three cancers diagnosed is skin cancer. When it is detected in its earliest stages the survival rate is around 97%, but that drops to only 14% if it goes detected until its latest stages (Kubota, 2017). Diagnosing skin cancer typically involves a visual examination. But AI can be even more accurate in skin cancer diagnosis. In one experiment AI was 95% accurate in diagnosing cancerous skin lesions compared to 86% accuracy by professional dermatologists (Haenssle et al., 2018). These results point to a need to develop a mobile app for skin cancer screening. It is very important for such an app to be available to everybody, including rural communities all over the world with no access to dermatologists (Comstock, 2018).

Artificial intelligence will help tackle some of the world's most challenging social welfare problems. In the paper "Notes from the AI Frontier: Applying AI for Social Good" (McKinsey, 2018a), researchers from the McKinsey Global Institute analyzed about 160 AI social impact use cases and classified them into ten different domains. They came to the conclusion that AI could potentially help hundreds of millions of people worldwide, in both developed and developing countries. It could be applicable to a range of issues, from diagnosing simple conditions to preventing natural disasters.

AI solutions in medicine are driven by the opportunity of significant savings. According to some estimates, in the United States AI solutions could potentially yield $150 billion in annual savings for the healthcare economy by 2026 (Accenture, 2017). The application that presents the most promise is virtual nursing. Patients can already receive a nurse consult 24/7 without having to leave their home. With no involvement by a doctor, a virtual medical assistant can quickly process a patient's complaints, find an optimal medical facility, connect to the required specialist and compare any previous and new test results. In some cases it can even prescribe medications and ensure more interactive and efficient communication between the doctor and patient, contributing to a significant reduction in clinic visits.

Through regular interactions with the patient, and access to their records and other important physiological indicators, virtual physicians can continue to learn and improve with a customized approach to each patient.

Another important benefit of artificial intelligence rapidly evolving in healthcare is the potential to reduce the huge administrative costs experienced by medical institutions. It is commonly known that often doctors have to perform administrative tasks that take away from the valuable time they have to spend with their patients. With its capabilities for speech to text recognition, today's AI can analyze patient-doctor conversations, record the patient's complaints, fill out medical records and write prescriptions.

As innovative systems help individual doctors, they can also assist in process management in medical centers. For example, Qventus,[29] an AI-based software platform, can analyze inefficiencies, optimize patient flow, issue alerts about lines or technical issues and offer optimal solutions to administrative problems. This system has already been implemented in a number of large medical centers across the United States.

Patients themselves also suffer economic losses. In the United States, people spend more than $200 billion annually to treat mental health issues (Roehrig, 2016). Yet 60% of mental health patients still do not receive all the care they need (Park-Lee et al., 2017). It is the most costly health problem in the country, and it continues to grow.

Amid such a lack of adequate patient care, Mindstrong uses machine learning to analyze brain function, cognitive abilities and people's states of mind by processing data about their use of smartphones, how they tap, move and do other things on their touch screens. The AI analysis showed very similar results to traditional neuropsychological diagnostics. Mindstrong launched its own app that processes this anonymized data and alerts its users of any changes in their mental health before they are able to notice them. Also, the app can perform case-specific psycho-logical interventions that complement therapy with the doctor or prevent complications from becoming something more serious. Additionally, a desktop app brings together patients and licensed mental health professionals into a single network, making their interactions easier and providing support around the clock.

Such progress in AI diagnostics makes it clear that in the near future, as virtual assistants learn more about patient-doctor interactions, they will improve their skills and be able to see and treat patients inde-pendently.

Another convincing example here is IBM Watson, a technology on which the company spent one billion US dollars back in 2014. In a broad sense, IBM Watson is a supercomputer with artificial intelligence that can understand humans, have a conversation with them and answer any questions thanks to its access to a huge 200 million-page database about virtu-ally everything. However, one of the first areas IBM Watson became an expert at was healthcare. The supercomputer has been helping treat cancer since

2013, having previously processed 1.5 million medical records (Steadman, 2013).

Today it is used in many large medical centers around the world, where it analyzes all available patient information and shows the oncologist the most important highlights. It can detect pathology and find the most optimal treatment for each patient. Watson is also constantly self-improving. It keeps abreast of the latest medical advances by reviewing millions of reports, medical records, clinical trials and articles in authoritative medical publications.

AI advances in medicine demonstrate real results in improving the efficiency of healthcare and therefore public welfare. However, the field could have had even more success stories, if not for some hurdles developers had to face. The first significant obstacle in the way of applying artificial intelligence to medicine is national quality control agencies.

In most countries, these organizations are simply not prepared for the breakthrough advances of the new era of technology. They are conservative and present too many bureaucratic hurdles. The oldest and largest such agency, the US Food and Drug Administration (FDA), takes on average seven years to approve a new medical device, with the average cost to develop one estimated at almost $100,000,000 (Gaur, 2017). But its appreciation of AI's enormous potential nevertheless led the FDA to create a separate department consisting of artificial intelligence experts.

The caution regulatory agencies exercise with respect to AI is understandable. It is partly due to the fact that most people still do not have a clear understanding of what artificial intelligence capabilities have already become a reality. According to a survey of healthcare executives (Faggella, 2019), AI adoption in healthcare is hindered by general industry conservatism and the need for cases studies to prove return on investment. New AI products are too complicated for most healthcare staff, who lack sufficient experience with smart technology.

We live in a time of constant discovery of new AI applications in medicine. Most examples mentioned have been implemented just in the last two or three years. New shared algorithms, access to terabytes of medical data, and the engagement of international organizations and business communities will help expand the application of artificial intelligence, making a reality out of what just recently seemed like science fiction.

Many experts agree that AI is not supposed to replace people in the workplace, but rather to provide a significant improvement in performance by reducing the risk of critical errors. As confirmed by the latest artificial intelligence successes, the best results are achieved with people and AI working together.

A large amount of medical information and the latest technology using artificial intelligence not only provides more accurate diagnoses and more effective treatment. It also make healthcare more personalized and accessible around the world, including in Kazakhstan.

Healthcare 2.0

Virtual assistants

When it comes to artificial intelligence, most people do not think of neural networks, which use deep learning to process and analyze large data sets. Rather, we have an image of a "speaking program" that can answer questions, make predictions, and actively participate in our life, one with its own personality.

Without a doubt, the best-known example of such an "animate" AI in today's world is Siri. This application was acquired by Apple back in 2010, two years after its official release. It was developed by SRI International's Artificial Intelligence Center and was the result of a 40-year AI development program funded by DARPA, the agency within the US Department of Defense mentioned above. This, by the way, once again confirms the military's long-standing interest in artificial intelligence.

Today, every user of mobile apps or an iPhone knows about Siri. The intelligent assistant, as Apple calls it, is a cloud-based application which is part of the company's different operating platforms. Siri supports a wide range of user commands, performs various tasks and answers questions. Its main feature is smart voice recognition, verbal communication with the user, constant learning, and flexibility, which means it will also clarify missing information when receiving ambiguous commands.

Just like other Apple products, Siri quickly became popular all over the world. Currently, Siri is able to make calls, send and read messages, schedule events and reminders, search for and remember music, do calculations, answer questions, order a taxi, get directions and do many other simple tasks using voice commands. But despite a rather wide range of useful features, Siri's capabilities have not changed as much as many have expected in its almost ten years of existence.

This delay is often blamed on the late launch of SiriKit, a tool for third-party developers, which appeared only in 2016, six years after the release of the assistant. With this tool, developers can add customized features to help integrate Siri fully into third-party apps.

Just a short time after the successful launch of the world's first voice assistant, the competition started heating up. In 2014, Microsoft introduced its intelligent assistant, and in 2016 Amazon and Google joined the race. In 2017, Yandex, a Russian company, started claiming market share in the CIS countries. Apple's competitors integrated Siri's capabilities into their own products and made them open-source from the very beginning. Amazon even pays developers for building popular Alexa skills, motivating programmers from all over the world.

The beneficial marketing integration makes the openness of virtual assistants very advantageous for both their creators and the owners of other software products. Intelligent assistant users start using apps with voice command features more often, and learn how to control the apps with voice commands. The key advantages for voice assistant companies have been in expanded product capabilities compared to the competition.

Voice assistants mainly rely on natural language processing. This non-trivial task involves choosing the correct meaning from many possible interpretations. Teaching an artificial intelligence to intuitively understand everyday human speech became possible because of a breakthrough in deep learning technology in the mid-2000s. The teaching process itself is complex and time consuming. It requires artificial intelligence to recognize and understand large samples of dialog spoken in different languages, dialects and accents.

A voice assistant is very useful for active users of standard applications on their devices. It's great for time management, including scheduling and setting reminders, and for navigating. However, the most universal feature of virtual assistants is being able to quickly search for answers. That is why the technology is alternatively known as a "question and answer system." In this sense, Google, Microsoft or Yandex, with their search engines, have a certain advantage.

However, simply understanding natural speech and performing a fast and efficient search is no longer enough. One of the main challenges for AI developers was teaching their programs to consider the context, which involves analyzing an enormous number of factors.

The first of these factors is the history of previous queries. If a user asks, "Where is the nearest subway station?" and then continues by asking, "What is the fastest way to get to it?" the voice assistant has to be able to understand what the user means by "it." Secondly, the assistant also needs to consider the situation surrounding the query and numerous other factors ranging from location, time of day and the user's schedule to ambient sounds and the user's possible movements at the time of the query. Third, it's very important for the assistant to know in advance and adapt to the user's habits. To do this, other than learning from queries, it needs to study each user to be able to better understand their intentions at a personal level.

A customized approach is the strongest card in the hand of any artificial intelligence developer, especially a virtual assistant developer. We can find a lot of different videos of users trying to converse with their voice assistants. Some voice assistants are better at it than others.

For example, Yandex's assistant, Alice, can tell funny stories and respond with jokes in certain situations.[30] In general, the Yandex helper is distinguished from competitors by a brighter personality—this is a young woman who has a sense of humor and irony, but is able to offer tactful resistance in the event of attacks by users. Alice's qualities give users a feeling of lively and easy interaction when communicating with her, while Yandex's vast experience developing search algorithms makes Alice a great helper in accomplishing a wide range of tasks.

One of the latest to appear, at the end of 2017, Alice quickly caught up and largely overtook competitors from Apple, Amazon and Google (Khokhlova, 2017). Since March 2018, Alice has become open to learning new skills from third-party developers. Over the course of just one year, Alice was taught tens of thousands of new skills, the best of which became available to all users. In addition to managing the standard functions of a smartphone, Alice can order a product, play games, read fairy tales to a child, sing a song, and perform many other unusual skills. In addition, one of Alice's most important tasks is to control the user's smart home using a system of speakers and microphones. Dozens of leading manufacturers of electronics and home appliances are planning to actively integrate their products with this smart home control platform.[31]

Another giant in the voice assistant market is Xiaoice, Microsoft's virtual conversation partner, developed in 2014 in the Chinese division of the corporation. The developers focused on developing its conversational skills, equipping it with not just artificial intelligence, but empathy. At the same time, Xiaoice not only adjusts to the emotions of its interlocutor, but also identifies various groups of users according to their interests and needs, building an appropriate dialogue. In addition, the virtual interlocutor uses what is called "full-duplex speech," which allows it to communicate in both directions, minimizing the delay between question and answer. The combination of all these functions makes Xiaoice communication as close as possible to an ordinary conversation between two people.

Xiaoice is one of the most promising chatbots today, as evidenced by the huge number of registered users: 660 million worldwide (Si, 2018). Xiaoice is widely used in social networks such as Facebook and Weibo, as well as in the WeChat and QQ messengers. All these platforms allow ordinary users to integrate the

Xiaoice chatbot into their account, automating the processing of requests from other users.

Such a large audience allows Xiaoice to quickly learn and improve its skills, mastering various areas of human activity. Xiaoice, for example, has already written a collection of 139 poems[32] and released dozens of songs (Spencer, 2018), as well as a collection of artistic prints and color combinations for clothes ("Microsoft's Xiaoice," 2018). Moreover, the assistant works in television and radio as the host of dozens of daily programs (Soo, 2018). And this is not the limit of its capabilities.

Considering that the focus in the work of the intelligent interlocutor is on Chinese, Xiaoice has a very large development potential as it gradually masters other languages. Indeed, at the moment, the virtual interlocutor is fully deployed only in five countries: China, Japan, the US, India and Indonesia.

The voice assistants of today still lag significantly behind their robot counterparts from science fiction. A digital assistant that can make a call to a real person (to set up a meeting, for example) and discuss different time and place options and then choose the best one has not been invented yet.

The AI of today's virtual assistants does not yet have a sufficient level of intuitive understanding, since the tasks they can perform with confidence must rely on strict sets of parameters, rules and algorithms. But nevertheless, there is an example of an artificial intelligence that is able to communicate quite easily with a person on various topics. This is a robot named Sofia, developed by the Hong Kong company Hanson Robotics. Launched for the first time in 2015, the female robot has already participated in hundreds of events and television programs, giving many people confidence that artificial intelligence has reached human-like self-awareness.

The latter is not true for Sophia or for any other AI just yet. But Sophia is constantly learning and improving her communication skills, which many see as the conscious understanding of information. Additionally, she can walk well and tell people apart with the help of cameras which imitate human eyes. She can also recognize human speech, reproduce gestures and emotions, and make jokes.

Sophia has the skills to meet people and have a coherent dialog. She has given numerous interviews and in 2017 was introduced at the United Nations and had a brief interaction with UN Deputy Secretary-General Amina J. Mohammed. That same year, Sophia, a social humanoid, was granted citizenship in Saudi Arabia and thanked the country for the honor of being the first robot in the world to become a citizen.

Just like Siri, Sophia became very popular very quickly. Her interviews and other events created a continuous buzz. The creators of the first AI-powered humanoid robot are often criticized for overhyping her abilities. She is not perfect, but she is constantly updating herself. A small but interesting example of Sophia's ability to learn human habits was her learning to look directly at the camera and smile when photographed by a famous photographer (Mallonee, 2018).

Developers are not done yet. They plan to create a decentralized network for artificial intelligence running on blockchain, a type of social network for AI. Any developer will be able to upload their AI to the network, and there, these humanoid robots will be able to communicate with and continuously learn from other AIs. This initiative opens the door to creating the first prototypes of artificial general intelligence (AGI), which can first reach and then surpass human ability to perform any mental task.

Virtual assistants

The financial sector and machine learning

Today's technologies of in-depth analysis and machine learning make it possible to actively apply artificial intelligence in various areas of the financial market. In pursuit of competitive advantages, financial organizations are seeking to introduce smart technologies into their work, leading to a noticeable transformation of the entire financial sector.

Artificial intelligence provides an opportunity to more accurately analyze the behavior and preferences of consumers of financial services, assess risks, automate thousands of work processes, formulate a clear rationale for making financial decisions and much more.

In terms of the economic effect, the practice of applying smart technologies in the field of lending is very indicative. Here, AI provides a faster and more accurate assessment of the borrower's creditworthiness and possible risks. As a result, more reliable loans can be issued at lower costs.

Such technological solutions are actively used, in particular, by Sberbank, a leader in the development of AI in the post-Soviet space. The company has implemented AI in its system for rapid loans, called the Loan Factory. Thanks to internal intelligent systems and machine learning algorithms that analyze huge registries of various customer data, AI can significantly reduce the risk the bank will issue a bad loan. At the same time, the automation of these important and complex tasks made it possible to significantly reduce the time needed to consider applications and the number of employees involved. As a result, over 10 years of practical use of this system,

Sberbank issued loans totaling 12.3 trillion rubles (almost 200 billion US dollars).[33]

In addition to improving the reliability of loans, an artificial intelligence credit rating can be used to assess borrowers who do not have a credit history. The number of such borrowers is actively growing in developing countries. Start-ups have begun to appear that offer unique approaches in this area. These companies can function as independent lenders, or they can offer their software solutions for use by existing financial institutions.

Singapore's Lenddo start-up[34] uses AI to analyze creditworthiness on the basis of an applicant's "digital footprint," meaning the digital information about a person who grants access through a special application on a smartphone. Lenddo has focused on lending to newly minted members of the middle class. Within one application, machine learning algorithms analyze an average of more than 12,000 indicators of online human activity, using that information to calculate the person's credit rating. And all this in less than three minutes!

Thus, the Lenddo system becomes a unique intermediary between a borrower and a lender: on the one hand, it makes it easier for borrowers to access funds; on the other hand, it provides credit organizations with a qualitative credit rating, replenishing the organization's customer base with reliable borrowers.

Lenddo's algorithms have proven their unique value. The credit scoring giants FICO (FICO, 2016) and Experian (Cision, 2017) have both announced their cooperation, planning to use this technology as part of promoting their services in the fast-growing financial markets of India, Indonesia and Vietnam.

A no less impressive example of the use of AI in lending is the start-up ZestFinance,[35] founded by machine learning experts from Google and other high-tech companies. This company's main product is the Zaml credit underwriting platform. It also incorporates machine learning, which is used for credit models that improve the quality of loans issued.

ZestFinance considers one of the main advantages of its platform to be the visibility of the work of its algorithms, allowing it to overcome what is called the "black box problem," a phrase used to describe the difficulty of understanding AI decision-making processes. ZestFinance works in the field of consumer, commercial, mortgage and car loans and actively cooperates with Microsoft, Ford Credit, Discover Financial Services and many other world-famous corporations (Knapp, 2018; Ford, 2017; Andriotis, 2019). But probably the start-up's biggest success has been its collaboration with Baidu, the leader of China's search engine market, in which ZestFinance determines the creditworthiness of millions of Baidu users based on their online activity data (ZestFinance, 2016).

A start-up called Upstart,[36] founded by former senior employees at Google, predicts the creditworthiness of people using machine learning, complementing this information with traditional FICO credit ratings, loan history and income data. Predictive models built by artificial intelligence increase the accuracy of a person's credit rating by analyzing data on his education, including grades, SAT scores, areas of study, and work experience.

Upstart functions as an independent lender, and in the five years it has been in business, it has issued loans worth more than $3.8 billion. 60% of those loans were fully automated and issued in just half an hour on average. Such a high level of automation has become possible because Upstart uses artificial intelligence to model all the components of each loan, including repayments, prepayments, and late payments, and constantly improves its model based on actual data. As a result, almost 90% of the company's current and closed loans were repaid on time. This kind of accurate risk assessment is helping the company capture the market for unsecured consumer loans, offering borrowers more favorable terms.

The start-up examples above illustrate how a small group of tech enthusiasts, using AI, can change the lending market for entire countries. Their methods show that artificial intelligence can accurately predict creditworthiness even for people who do not have a borrowing history. In this case, a variety of data is used, whether it is activity in social networks, search query history, or grades at school.

At a large bank, the transition from traditional to innovative lending methods is a rather long and laborious process. At the same time, over-regulation of the banking sector in terms of lending often hampers the process of transition to smart technologies. Then there are the issues of employment and the corporate ecosystem; the introduction of machine learning promises layoffs for a huge number of loan managers, the need for whom is eliminated by the capabilities of AI. All this explains the inertia of banks when the size of the company begins to work against it. In this environment, it is only natural that dynamic new players are appearing on the financial market, demonstrating a clear trend towards a future in which the credit market will be entirely in the hands of artificial intelligence.

And yet the banking sector is not standing still. One of the most popular types of artificial intelligence applications is the use of chatbots at banks. It is no secret that the quality of customer service is a key factor in a bank's success. It involves a set of components: the speed of service, the accuracy and availability of information, personal contact with the client, the number of actions that the client must perform, and much more. A chatbot or virtual assistant, working on the basis of artificial intelligence, can improve the efficiency of service at each stage.

The largest US and UK financial conglomerates, such as Bank of America, JPMorgan Chase, Wells Fargo and HSBC, are investing billions of dollars in this technology. And this is not surprising, because chatbots have a number of serious advantages.

Firstly, virtual assistants guarantee customers an instant and round-the-clock response to their requests, which is much more convenient than long telephone calls to the bank's referral service, which in most cases is available only during working hours.

Secondly, chatbots are easy to use and greatly facilitate access to bank products and services. No matter how convenient and intuitive a mobile application might be, it is much easier for users to give a voice command to a chatbot and get instant access to digital banking features.

Thirdly, they mean personalization, which is one of the main advantages of machine learning. While it interacts with a client, a virtual assistant can also examine his requests, expenses, budget and other information about his financial behavior. A chatbot can keep records of expenses, display them in a user-friendly form and make relevant suggestions. It can calculate creditworthiness, give advice on savings and offer exactly those bank products and services that best suit the financial characteristics of the client.

All these advantages are demonstrated to some extent with real examples. For example, Erica, the virtual assistant from Bank of America, has already assisted more than six million users. In less than a year, the chatbot processed 35 million requests.[37]

Erica's skills include searching for completed transactions, booking a visit to a bank, displaying payments and scheduling them, transferring funds between accounts and using Zelle digital payments. In addition, Erica can notify customers in time when payment dates are approaching, set limits on spending and cash withdrawals, and provide information about the benefits that customers can receive under the various programs of the bank (Condon, 2018).

Unlike the Bank of America chatbot, which is integrated into the bank's mobile application, Wells Fargo's virtual assistant is implemented through Facebook Messenger and is designed to facilitate interaction with the bank by active users of Facebook. The assistant's functionality is a bit more modest than that of Erica, but the Wells Fargo chatbot can also quickly provide all the necessary information about bills, transactions, costs and locations of nearby ATMs and branches (Burnett, 2017).

Modern chatbots provided by banks generally have a similar set of skills: working with accounts, providing data on costs, transactions and payments, various alerts, booking visits to the bank, and also displaying reference information about branches and services of the bank. While this alone makes life much easier for customers and staff, there are other examples where using a virtual assistant leads to real transactions.

For example, OSVS Bank, one of the largest in Southeast Asia, has successfully launched the Emma program based on artificial intelligence, which handles requests for advice on loans for home purchases and renovations.[38] In the first four months after its launch, Emma successfully processed 20,000 requests, 10% of which led to actual loans. As a result, in less than a year of operation, the chatbot helped to issue mortgage loans worth $70 million (Lee, 2017), while 90% of customers were satisfied with their interaction with it. Emma is able not only to provide quality advice, but also to calculate the amount of the loan that the client can count on, and then lead the client through all stages of loan processing.

In the financial sector, as in other areas of the economy, automation plays a key role in reducing costs. Thus, according to some studies, merely automating certain tasks using AI can save the financial industry $1 trillion in the next 10 years (Kabza, 2019).

Meanwhile, artificial intelligence in combination with the optimization of business processes creates what is often called "intelligent automation." This, according to research by the Capgemini technology consultancy, will generate additional revenues of $512 billion in financial services, $243 billion in insurance and $269 billion in banking as soon as the year 2020 (Priyanka, 2018).

Without straying from the topic of virtual assistants, it is worth mentioning that today their potential is maximally revealed precisely as an auxiliary tool for a live consultant. Modern machine learning capabilities allow AI to analyze the work of help-desk operators and assist them in providing information.

Thanks to the introduction of this technology, Sberbank, for example, has reduced the average call duration to a call center to 3.5 minutes, which is 50% faster than before ("Robot," 2018). Finnish bank Nordea has implemented a similar artificial intelligence technology to automate the processing and forwarding of customer queries to the responsible department. The Estonian start-up Feelingstream has also advanced in the same direction, and its technology analyzes and classifies customer messages that are sent to the relevant sector for processing. It can analyze hundreds of messages per second, resulting in faster response times and improved customer interaction ("Swedish," 2017).

JPMorgan Chase has developed the Contract Intelligence (COiN) platform, designed to analyze legal documents, and in particular, loan agreements (JPMorgan, 2017). The bank thereby made life easier for its lawyers, because the volume of documents that the AI processes in a matter of seconds would require 360,000 man-hours of human labor.

Another trend in the development of automation in the financial sector is the active introduction of robotic process automation (RPA). While until recently automation required the extensive and time-consuming writing of complex computer code, newer solutions graphically recognize and record user actions and automatically generate code. However, the most advanced tools integrate artificial intelligence into this process, which itself recognizes actions, interface objects and text, combining them into uniform algorithms for automating business processes.

Many bank employees perform hundreds of the same actions on their computer every day, which takes up a significant portion of their working hours. In addition, the risk of errors increases. Therefore, many banks are actively integrating into their work the available tools for robotic automation. One example is Bank of New York Mellon. Back in 2017, it introduced more than 250 "virtual robots" developed by Blue Prism to automate certain processes.[39] JPMorgan Chase, for its part, chose to use Kofax robotic automation, software solutions that can increase productivity 35-50%, completely eliminate data entry errors, speed up the average processing time 30-50% and thus reduce the company's costs 25-50% (KOFAX, 2019).

In addition to increasing productivity and eliminating the human error factor, automation also brings to a new level other financial activities, such as stock trading. The main tasks of the trader are to analyze the market and complete trade transactions on the basis of that analysis. These functions can be fully automated with today's artificial intelligence capabilities. Intelligent trading systems can monitor hundreds of structured databases and process information from sources such as social networks and news portals. And they do all this at speeds beyond the limits of man.

According to a study by Inventure Recruitment, investments made on the basis of algorithmic trading exceeded $1 trillion in 2018. The trend is evident: back in 2000, 600 traders worked at the New York headquarters of the investment bank Goldman Sachs. Today, only two of them remain. The work of the rest is easily covered by automated trading programs that are serviced by 200 computer engineers. The role of the latter has increased significantly with the rapid development of technology, given that today their number in the company's headquarters is more than 9,000 people or a quarter of the entire staff (Byrnes, 2017).

Deutsche Bank, which launched its own security-trading platform with AI capabilities, Autobahn 2.0,[40] is moving in the same direction. This platform has a self-learning mechanism that improves the quality of forecast prices and stock volumes and, accordingly, crafts the best deals. Realizing the scale of possible automation, the management of Deutsche Bank has already announced that robots can realistically replace many professionals working in the bank, which will lead inevitably to reductions in staff (Noonan, 2017).

The price forecasting system Alpaca.AI was launched by Bloomberg, one of the world's leading providers of financial information. With the help of artificial intelligence, the system identifies patterns of price fluctuations that are hidden to humans, helping in the work of traders and investors.

Another media corporation, Nikkei, is creating its own AI-based software that predicts fluctuations in the Forex market. Despite the fact that the program is still at the development stage, it has already proven its effectiveness by winning Nikkei's quarterly contest to predict the dollar-yen exchange rate (Takahashi, 2018).

When it comes to the use of artificial intelligence in the financial sector, it is impossible not to mention its contribution to flagging cases of fraud, which is becoming a more frequent problem due to the development of e-commerce and online transactions. According to a PWC survey, in 2018, almost half (49%) of organizations around the world indicated that they had been the victim of fraud or economic crime. Moreover, half of these crimes (52%) were committed within the organization itself, while cyberattacks were noted in a third of cases (31%) (PWC, 2018b).

Artificial intelligence has already proven its effectiveness in detecting fraud. It is especially good at preventing credit card fraud, which has been growing rapidly in recent years. Mastercard, for example, developed the Decision Intelligence security platform, which uses machine learning technology. Analyzing real-time account data, the system has specific deviation thresholds and independently issues alerts when it detects abnormal behavior in purchases and other transactions. Thus, the system can quickly respond to cases of fraud and prevent theft of funds.[41]

A similar approach is used by Sberbank, whose intelligent BI.ZONE system, analyzing hundreds of customer parameters, reveals anomalous behavior in financial management. Based on data on the use of the bank's mobile application, information on purchases, payment methods and other variables, the system forms a pattern of the individual's digital financial behavior. The strength of this approach is the fact that the digital behavior of a person almost never changes, so any deviations from the norm are an almost one hundred percent guarantee that fraud is underway.[42]

In addition to defining anomalies in a person's digital behavior, AI-based financial protection tools are serving other purposes as well. For example, thanks to the development of technologies for identifying individuals, facial recognition biometrics or, as they are sometimes called, "selfie payments," are becoming increasingly popular in banks and payment systems (Mastercard, 2015). When a person makes a purchase using a card or a payment account, he must confirm it by scanning his face through a mobile application on a smartphone.

To identify anomalies, artificial intelligence uses a variety of data: geo-coordinates, the frequency of clicks on a smartphone, the height at which the person holds the phone, and much more. Experts in the field of AI and financial security are combining their efforts and creating new solutions and start-ups, covering the fast-growing e-commerce market. Thousands of companies of various types, including large banks, are beginning to use their software solutions.

For example, JPMorgan Chase has long been working with Kount,[43] one of the leaders in the market for innovative fraud detection solutions for the digital business. And HSBC has partnered with the start-up Quantexa, whose AI-based software can detect money laundering, fraud and terrorist financing (Arnold, 2018).

Realizing how useful AI can be for charting the digital habits of their customers, financial institutions have begun to actively explore its potential in terms of increasing the personalization of their products.

Personalization is something that is achieved in one way or another by almost all the smart solutions that we have touched upon in this section. Smart credit rating platforms allow financial institutions to find the perfect balance between risk and opportunity at the individual level. Chatbots and support systems in call centers examine customer requests in order to improve the quality of service for each individual. Smart security systems that protect customers from financial fraud are doing the same.

The development of algorithms that study people's digital behavior has launched an increasingly popular trend to personalize mobile applications. Of course, this promises a huge profit, considering that, for example, almost 50 million people use the Sberbank app. Taking advantage of its extensive experience using AI in its activities and products, Sberbank has now implemented AI in its app, which will now adapt to each client according to his preferences. Assessment takes place based on more than 1000 parameters, which allows the artificial intelligence to automatically change the application interface, providing faster access to the most popular operations.

With the development of mobile banking, apps that allow you to optimize costs and manage savings will also become more popular. One of the leaders in creating smart financial management platforms is the Israeli company Personetics Technologies, whose solutions are used by six of the twelve largest banks in North America and Europe, including Wells Fargo, Royal Bank of Canada, BNP Paribas and others (Penn, 2018). In its products, the company uses a combination of machine learning, natural language processing, and AI-based predictive analytics. Banks use Personetics services to offer their users an interactive app that is able to set financial goals and find the best ways to achieve them. Meanwhile, a chatbot contacts the client to offer tips on savings and to warn him when he is deviating from his financial plans.

Today, AI is beginning to be used by almost all leading banks, as well as large financial and analytical organizations (Equifax (Nordqvist, 2019) and SAS,[44] for example), which indicates the entire industry is dynamically transitioning to a new high-tech reality. The market for financial services is being stormed by

technology start-ups in a way that is actively changing its landscape and the rules of the game. Large
banks, despite their age, simply cannot afford to be
conservative. Given that financial flows increasingly
go into the digital dimension, and an army of millen-
nials has started along the path to financial independence, the competitive struggle in the financial sector is being transferred to the field of implementing
smart chatbots and personalized applications, minimizing risks and maximally automating all business
processes.

A new transportation architecture

One of the most rapidly evolving AI fields today is automated driving systems, the most famous part of which is autonomous vehicles. And according to forecasts, this trend will only accelerate. Some experts say the market will triple in the next five years,[45] while others expect it to increase almost by a factor of ten (Kumar, 2018). But absolutely everyone agrees about one thing: self-driving cars are an inevitable part of our future.

Why is there such confidence on this score? The answers are pretty obvious. First of all, artificial intelligence can drive more safely than a human driver, and that's important for a lot of countries with high traffic-related death rates, including Kazakhstan (WHO, 2017). According to the latest data from the World Health Organization (WHO, 2018), traffic accidents caused an estimated 1.35 million deaths worldwide (3,000-4,000 people per day) in 2016 and injured tens of millions of people. Traffic accidents are the leading cause of death for people between 5 and 29 years old.

Other advantages of autonomous vehicles include more productive time for commuters, transportation options that are more accessible and affordable, and improved traffic control, as well as economic benefits and reduced emissions.

The degree of autonomy in vehicles varies, and five levels can be distinguished. The first two include long-established capabilities in some vehicles, including cruise control and lane centering. Starting with level three, vehicles can be called self-driving. This level includes vehicles with partial automation under certain traffic or environmental conditions, as in the use of autopilot when in traffic or on the freeway.

But in some situations a driver is still necessary in level 3 cars, so they need to be equipped with a fully-equipped driver's seat. Level 4 vehicles have high automation and in most situations do not need the same level of human control. Finally, level 5 refers to a fully autonomous system able to operate without a human driver in every driving scenario.

Because the combination of manual and autonomous control modes and switching between them may present additional risk of accidents, autonomous car developers have been focusing on creating level-4 vehicles. This focus makes sense in view of well-publicized accidents, such as the Uber self-driving vehicle that struck and killed a pedestrian (Stilgoe, 2019).

While level 4 cars have been tested on the roads, large scale production has not yet begun, though one estimate cited 2025 as the take-off year (Walker, 2019). What we have now is a true technology race in which such tech giants as Google and Apple are competing against the automakers. That is no surprise, considering that the global automobile market is worth hundreds of billions of dollars. Safety is an important factor for automakers, so those who are able to create the first truly safe, fully autonomous driving system will be poised to keep their leading position for a long time.

The current leader in the autonomous driving market is Waymo One, a project by Alphabet Inc. and its subsidiary, Google. The company started testing their first self-driving technology before anybody else, back in 2009. It had the advantage of having access to Google Street View, a feature of Google Maps that provides interactive panoramas along city streets. These maps were an integral part of launching a full trial of self-driving vehicles in real road conditions where AI could learn, practice and improve its driving skills.

After almost seven years of testing, at the end of 2016, Alphabet set up a subsidiary, Waymo, which two years later unveiled its first commercial driverless taxi service. But access to the service was limited to a few hundred riders who had participated in the early testing in a handful of neighborhoods in Phoenix, Arizona. It was still a success: before the launch Waymo's market capitalization was estimated at $175 billion (Rapier, 2018), while afterwards the company was valued at $250 billion (Ungarino, 2018).

Such numbers tempted many companies to try and find their niche in the relatively empty autonomous vehicle market. Ten years of investment into the Waymo project have more than paid off for Alphabet. The company is now valued at $766 billion and ranks third on the Forbes list of the world's largest public companies.[46]

Waymo is rightly considered to have the most experienced "virtual driver," and it has now driven 10 million miles on public roads in 20 American cities. The company is interested in spreading its technology to other countries, but in recent years, the autonomous taxi manufacturer has faced a serious competitor: Yandex.

Yandex and Google are very similar: each offers a search engine, map service, electronic commerce, media resources and much more. But Yandex is also known for its online taxi order service with wide geographical coverage: 300 large cities in 16 countries. Extensive experience in all these industries helped the company introduce its own autonomous taxi project in 2017. Since then, Yandex has begun active testing of its technologies in Moscow and in the Tatarstan technology park of Innopolis, which is officially a city, albeit a very small one. In addition, in early 2019, the Yandex autonomous car based on the Toyota Prius model chauffeured participants at the CES international exhibition in Las Vegas (Kiniakina, 2019). Yandex is also actively creating its own research and development center in Tel Aviv, where foreign companies are allowed to test autonomous vehicles on public roads ("Iandeks nachnet," 2019). Aside from that case, autonomous driving is only possible—with local consent—in the United States.

Yandex's potential for autonomous vehicle control makes it one of the favorites in the race to develop the drone taxi market. The company has already signed an agreement with the South Korean company Hyundai Mobis on the joint creation of software and hardware, which can then be integrated into cars of various makes and models. By the end of 2019, Yandex plans to expand its fleet of test cars to 100 ("Iandeks uvelichit," 2019), and the company says the full-fledged launch of an autonomous taxi may occur as early as 2022 ("Iandeks ne iskliuchil," 2019).

Training the on-board artificial intelligence remains the key to creating a reliable system that will have a comprehensive set of data and actions it can take in any situation on the road. What makes it possible is a whole range of sensors including cameras, radars and a lidar unit — the key technology behind the "vision" of self-driving vehicle.

Introduced in 2007, lidar is a sensor that fires millions of laser beams and precisely measures the reflected pulses. Thus a self-driving vehicle receives the contours of surrounding objects from radar and 2D camera images, and it also can use a dynamic 3D map of all objects in a radius of about 300 yards. To a large extent, the future of autonomous vehicles depends on the development of more economical and more reliable lidar technology, which for now is still very expensive and limited in its capabilities.

The training of autonomous driving systems not only improves their AI driving skills, but also produces high-resolution maps with centimeter-level accuracy. Such precision is extremely important in teaching AI to identify various objects: from the road surface, vehicles and road signs to people, animals and smaller objects. What is also important is not just the location of an object but also its nature, in order to allow AI to predict its future behavior. For example, at this stage even Waymo, the most experienced system, cannot tell a piece of paper from a stone or a pedestrian from a police officer. Making such distinctions is essential; otherwise a driverless system is doomed to make the wrong decisions. Also, bad weather conditions significantly reduce an autonomous vehicle's ability to perceive space. On snow-covered roads the sensors become almost useless. Therefore, highly detailed virtual maps are very important for autonomous driving under variable conditions.

Another challenge facing autonomous vehicles is regulation. Any testing of potentially dangerous self-driving vehicles can only happen with legislative approval. The United States pioneered this process, with regulatory changes beginning in 2011. Today, self-driving vehicle testing has been approved in half of the US states (NCSL, 2019). Germany and other countries followed suit in 2017 with Russia joining the process at the end of 2018. Legal regulations might include a number of limitations (speed limits or the presence of a human driver) and depend to a considerable extent on infrastructure, roads and other local conditions.

In this regard, many countries still need reforms to keep up with testing autonomous vehicles, while states with more flexible laws have begun to develop innovative transport without facing legal barriers. For example, the laws of Finland did not initially spell out the need for a driver in a car, thanks to which autonomous electric minibuses from the Japanese company Muji and French company NAVYA are already running on the roads of Helsinki (Hitti, 2019a; Lemola, 2018).

Muji and NAVYA are also actively promoting their eco-friendly robotic buses in other countries, including France, Germany, Switzerland, the Netherlands, Sweden, the United States, Singapore, Australia, and Canada. Japanese developers, meanwhile, are placing their bets on making their buses reliable in all types of weather and covering passengers in hard-to-reach areas. The company also has plans to occupy a niche for the autonomous delivery of goods. That service is certainly an extensive area in which autonomous vehicles could be used. FedEx, a world leader in fast package delivery, plans to start testing its SameDay Bot in several US cities in the summer of 2019 (Hitti, 2019b). A small robot courier uses special machine learning algorithms and a wheel control system to overcome various obstacles, climb stairs, and deliver goods door-to-door.

The German car manufacturer Continental chose a more original way to reach the buyer's door: their autonomous minibuses will transport the famous robot dogs developed by Boston Dynamics, which easily overcome various unpredictable obstacles, and also know how to open doors and move objects (Aouf, 2019a). The minibus selects several destination addresses in one area, travels to the optimum point, and then releases four-legged couriers with the packages.

While some manufacturers of autonomous robots are testing their solutions, others are actively exploring the market. For instance, the Starship project, launched by the co-founders of Skype, had made 30,000 deliveries as of February 2019.

A no less promising application of AI in the transport sector is in large-scale freight. In urban environments there are many different factors and difficult-to-predict scenarios that need to be considered to avoid accidents, but trucking on dedicated highways is a much more straightforward process. Heavy vehicles spend most of their time on the highway, where there are practically no traffic lights, intersections, pedestrians, etc. Thus, freight transportation offers near-term opportunities for third-level autonomous transport, in which the driver's functions can be partially shifted to artificial intelligence.

At present, developers of automated piloting systems and automotive manufacturers are actively cooperating to develop the market for autonomous trucks. Waymo, mentioned above, as well as companies such as TuSimple, Embark, Tesla, Volvo, Daimler and others, are already testing their autonomous trucks on public roads. This race is understandable. According to the American Freight Association,[47] more than 70% of the cargo delivered in the United States is carried by trucks, with a market estimated at $726 billion (Nodal, 2019). Despite such big numbers, the industry is experiencing difficult times. Pay for drivers has been decreasing in real terms (Premack, 2018), prompting them to withdraw from the market (Mpetey, 2019). The reduction in the number of truck drivers amid a booming online sales market creates ideal conditions for the launch of autonomous cargo shipments.

Still, the manufacturers of autonomous trucks are not about to refuse the services of drivers; the current implementation of level 3 and 4 autonomous vehicles significantly facilitates, but does not replace, drivers' work. While artificial intelligence drives a truck, the driver can rest, which in the future will allow them to be on the road 24 hours a day, completing 2.5 times more orders.

Such an efficient use of trucks can significantly reduce the load on the roads and fuel consumption and, consequently, reduce environmental damage. Given the accelerating progress of electric cars, the economic impact of highly efficient, fast and environmentally friendly cargo delivery by an autonomous electric truck can give a powerful impetus to the development of many industries that depend on freight.

The participation of artificial intelligence in freight shipping is not limited to driving. Big data processing systems and machine learning algorithms can optimize traffic flows, provide continuous monitoring of vehicles and road conditions, predict traffic congestion and prevent shortages of shipping units. Taking into account all of this and other possibilities, artificial intelligence will radically change the look of the freight industry and bring logistic solutions to a new level.

In other words, artificial intelligence will not fully take the driver's seat. On the contrary: by simplifying the work of truckers, automation solutions will attract new people to the industry, offsetting the current and projected shortage of truck drivers.

Safety will also improve. Large trucks are involved in many accidents caused by driver fatigue. According to some estimates, artificial intelligence can reduce the number of accidents involving trucks by 80% in the next 20 years (Calderone, 2018).

Amazon, the market leader in online sales, is striving to create its own offline delivery design. Known for its ambitious and innovative projects, Amazon is now aiming for the world's fastest delivery, by using drones. At the re:MARS conference in Las Vegas, organized by Amazon owner Jeff Bezos, it was said that autonomous air delivery might begin as early as 2019 (Hitti, 2019c).

If goods can be delivered with a drone, then why not make the drone a car? Flying cars already exist. Boeing, Airbus, Lilium and others are actively involved in testing, while Uber and the Dubai Road Transport Agency are planning the imminent launch of an air taxi service (Aouf, 2019b; Hitti, 2018a; Morby, 2017a; Gibson, 2017; Morby, 2017b). Flying autonomous vehicles have already been presented by the Chinese company Ehang[48] and the Dutch company Pal-V (Hitti, 2018b). Many other companies have also joined the race for autonomous air transport, and it seems likely that we will see the actual use of autonomous air transport in the foreseeable future.

Drones and autonomous flying vehicles are even beginning to change the face of modern cities. Some of the latest house designs are beginning to offer landing and take-off spaces for flying couriers (Ravenscroft, 2019), while the British Skyports company is actively buying rooftops in London in order to create a network of pads for the vertical take-off and electrical recharging of drones, which, the company believes, will become a commonplace part of the urban infrastructure (Fairs, 2018).

The capabilities of autonomous vehicles can be applied in almost any field. In construction, they can quickly deliver materials and make accurate measurements. In healthcare they can deliver medicines to patients, in policing they can monitor violations, in agriculture they can fertilize the soil and perhaps even harvest crops. They can conduct continuous monitoring of emergency situations and perhaps prevent their escalation, provide essential supplies for the victims of natural disasters, and help with other difficult-to-control threats.

As the first autonomous buses and taxis enter into operation, along with trucks and drones, the first self-steering ships are also being launched ("Rolls-Royce," 2018). Much remains to be done to fully adapt artificial intelligence systems to real-life conditions, while legal barriers to testing are still in need of revision, or abrogation.

The testing of autonomous vehicles in real-life conditions largely depends on local conditions. Certainly, the transition to autonomous driving will require many changes in road transport infrastructure everywhere. Moreover, because autonomous cars will continue to encounter difficulties in analyzing the environment, other sources of information must come to the rescue. First and foremost, autonomous vehicles must constantly communicate with each other via V2V (vehicle-to-vehicle) technology, something that could significantly reduce the number of accidents.[49] In the near future, V2V communications may become mandatory for all new cars. Unmanned vehicles will also need to receive signals from infrastructure such as buildings, road signs and protective barriers. A unique signal should be emitted by all smartphones and identification sensors used by the police, ambulances and other services.

Seaports and ships are beginning to be equipped with tracking devices and sensors that allow for trouble-free mooring and shipping, while airports and train stations are progressively implementing smart security, traffic optimization and fault-monitoring systems. What's more, the Industrial Internet of Things (IIoT) is becoming a limitless space for the intelligent interaction of electrical appliances and deep analytics, achieving new levels of efficiency. The improvement of smart technologies and deep analytics creates an additional impetus to the development of autonomous transport.

The readiness of countries to accept autonomous vehicles depends on several factors: the level of the relevant technologies, infrastructure, legislation and of course consumer acceptance. KPMG has developed an Autonomous Vehicles Readiness Index ranking 20 countries in the race toward a future with autonomous vehicles (KPMG, 2018). From top to bottom, the top five countries in the list are the Netherlands, Singapore, US, Sweden and the United Kingdom. The bottom-ranked countries are China, Brazil, Russia, Mexico and India.

Obviously, in the next five to ten years, most countries will begin to switch to this new type of transportation technology. It is important for Kazakhstan to participate in the process of change, both because of its potential economic importance and because of the expected gains in safety, logistical efficiency, traffic management, infrastructure costs, reduced pollution, and increased mobility. That in turn has the potential to reduce social stressors and "transportation inequality." Taken together, these factors offer tremendous prospects.

Smart cities

Modern cities occupy only 2% of the surface of our planet. However, this is a very active 2%, generating 80% of global GDP, 80% of all CO_2 emissions and 75% of resource consumption (Swilling, 2013). At the same time, cities continue to develop and grow: according to UN forecasts, by 2050, the proportion of people living in urban areas will increase from today's 55.2% to 68% (United Nations, 2018). The rapid growth of the urban population exacerbates the problems of environmental pollution, congestion and lack of resources such as land, energy and water.

All these issues cannot be solved by traditional management methods. Only by using modern science and technology in urban planning, construction and management, such as the Internet of Things, cloud computing, big data, geographic information and spatial analysis, will it become possible to manage a city effectively. Therefore, the Smart City is not just a new approach to solving the problems posed by urbanization, but also a framework for accelerating industrialization, digitalization and, as a result, national economic growth.

Smart cities consist of interconnected networks of various devices and sensors, with each network responsible for one major function, such as the optimization of the water supply and drainage, with another for traffic control, a third one for fire safety, a fourth to monitor pollution levels, a fifth to control crime, and more. Most important, all smart city networks can actively interact with each other, greatly increasing the overall efficiency of the entire system, the smart city itself. The traffic control system, for example, analyzes congestion and accident risks, increasing the efficiency of emergency, firefighting and medical services. Thus, the complex architecture of interconnected networks creates an urban management platform. It helps in the search for new AI-based solutions for constant situation monitoring and analysis, forecasting and optimal decision making.

Today, most data in smart city platforms is generated by photo and video cameras. This situation is not going to change in the near future. NVIDIA, the world leader in visual computing, estimates that by 2020 there will be a billion cameras deployed on government property, public transit, commercial buildings and roadways, capturing 30 billion images per second (NVIDIA, 2017).

Analyzing all that data is the main challenge for the effectiveness of smart city platforms, and there is much work in progress. For example, the Metropolis intelligent video analytics platform applies deep learning to video streams. Metropolis works with a network of smart cameras equipped with their own hardware and software. Video analytics is used for such applications as business process optimization, traffic management and public safety in government agencies, shopping malls, etc.

Video analytics can quickly help find a missing person, detect thefts and other crimes, manage traffic in stores, warehouses and parking lots, record health and safety violations in manufacturing, etc. However, no matter how "smart" the cameras are, they don't capture all the vital processes in an urban environment.

In addition to improving security and energy efficiency and optimizing the strain on infrastructure, the smart city concept offers itself up as the solution to vital issues of social inequality. This is achieved by increasing the access of citizens from less privileged areas to the highest quality services. However, first of all, a smart city must be provided with infrastructure that strengthens social ties between representatives of different communities living in the same city. This can mean streets, squares, parks, cultural centers—in a word, any places that strengthen social interaction and unite people around the city.

Helsinki, for example, has the free Oodi library,[50] which is a public venue for cultural activity. It is equipped with a cinema, an auditorium, studios, cafes and a co-working area.

In Toronto, Sidewalk Labs, an innovative urban infrastructure development company, has invested 1.3 billion US dollars to create an entire neighborhood that will include various social integration solutions.[51] For example, all spaces are designed with an eye to convenience for pedestrians and bicycle riders. All the infrastructure is adapted for people with disabilities.

However, it is not necessary to create socially conscious infrastructure from scratch. For example, some areas in Barcelona have been reorganized into self-sufficient blocks, provided with all necessary services and public entertainment facilities (Roberts, 2017).

Electronic platforms can also be the basis for social integration. For example, New York, one the "smartest" cities in the world, decided to make the data it collects completely open. Anyone can use NYC Opendata[52] for research or commercial purposes. This initiative has brought together researchers, scientists and developers to solve various problems facing the city and improve the well-being of its inhabitants. Thousands of studies have been carried out on the basis of NYC Opendata and thousands of analytic systems, applications, ideas and reviews have been created.

Smart cities need a very wide range of quality data, and universal sensors are required for the collection of this data. San Diego might be one of the most significant examples of this: in 2017, some 3,200 smart sensing lights, designed and operated by Current, a subsidiary of General Electric, were installed in the city. They look like regular LED streetlights, but in addition to energy efficient light bulbs, they include a number of different sensors and cameras.

The sensor nodes are powered by a network created by AT&T, the largest telecommunications company in the world. Today it helps to improve parking, traffic, public safety and the environment, improving the quality of urban life. The San Diego authorities, just like their New York counterparts, are making the collected data available to all. It is now used by students, researchers, coders and businesses to write apps that serve their own needs and to provide new insights in the analysis of the smart urban environment.

The system comes with economic benefits as well: after the initial investment of $30 million, San Diego has saved $2.4 million annually on LED lighting alone. The economic impact of an entire city platform powered by AI is much higher.

Across the world, many big metropolitan areas have launched smart city pilots. In China, 154 cities are working on their own smart projects. Launched in 2016, Hangzhou's "City Brain" project, created by the Chinese corporation Alibaba, uses camera systems and sensors across the city to collect data on road conditions in real time. The data is fed to an AI hub, which then manages traffic signals at 128 intersections, helping city officials make better decisions at a faster pace.

One telling example: the system tracks ambulances en route to hospitals and turns all the red lights in their path to green, allowing patients to receive timely emergency care. In fact, City Brain has cut traveling times for ambulances in half. The program has also allowed the Hangzhou police force to operate more efficiently. The smart city system can detect accidents within seconds, allowing the police to arrive at the scene in five minutes or less.

To solve Shanghai's public parking problems, Chinese tech giant Huawei launched a smart parking network that allows car users to find, book and pay for nearby parking spots from a special smartphone app. Chips are embedded beneath parking spaces in over 300 parking lots across the city. They transmit real-time information on the occupancy rate of each lot. Drivers can just look up nearby vacancies on the app and then pay to use them.

In South Korea, following the opening of Incheon International Airport, three new smart town developments were created in the city of Incheon. The smart city project in Songdo, for example, is connected by a single communication network with private businesses and public agencies. A specialized service in Songdo is utilizing RFID[53] and USN[54] technology to provide environmentally friendly services (for example, U-bike or U-street). The same technology is also used for crime prevention, with cameras recording vehicle registration numbers that are able to pick out stolen vehicles, those with unpaid taxes or fines, and so on.

In these projects, the buildings have LEED[55] certification. IoT sensors are installed in houses and buildings in Songdo to provide real-time information to users about how much energy has been consumed and what measures can be taken to minimize utility bills. Using smart mobile applications, users can turn off electric devices and control the temperature and lighting of their houses and apartments just by touching their smartphones.

Here's another interesting detail: there are no garbage cans or garbage trucks in Songdo. All household waste is moved directly through an underground network of tunnels by a smart pneumatic system and then sorted, recycled or discarded. The city has also been equipped with sensors to monitor temperature, energy use and traffic flow (Lee, 2016).

Masdar City in the UAE was originally designed as a city without cars and zero carbon emissions for a daytime population of 70,000 people. The concept has since been improved and expanded and now Masdar is known all over the world as a smart city of the future, along with Meixi (China), Padua (Italy), SmartCity (Malta), PlanIT Valley (Portugal) and Lavasa (India), which are also being built from scratch (Hall, 2000).

In Masdar, only sustainable construction materials are utilized. Special designs are used to change wind direction and reduce direct sunlight on sidewalks. Each yard of every rooftop is covered with solar panels. In October 2018, the city officially launched an autonomous electric shuttle service built by the French company NAVYA. The self-driving electric vehicle carries up to 12 people, is fully autonomous and has a top speed of 25km/h ("Masdar," 2018). In January of this year Masdar City unveiled a farming showcase called "Bustani" to demonstrate new farming solutions that will help UAE residents produce their own food at home ("Masdar," 2019).

In the fall of 2017, Saudi Arabia announced a new project: a megacity called Neom. The name itself signifies a breakthrough as its two parts translate as "The New Future." The project has an estimated initial cost of $500 billion, which is more than the 2019 GDP of Austria, UAE or Norway (IMF, 2019). Neom's planned total area of 26,500 km2 is larger than that of fifty different independent countries, including Rwanda and Macedonia.

Neom will incorporate cutting-edge smart city technologies and function as a special economic zone and tourist destination with its own laws aimed at facilitating investment. Plans call for the city to be powered solely with wind and solar power. Robots will perform most of the jobs such as security, logistics, home delivery, and caregiving. It is expected that there will be more robots in the city than residents.

The large scale, high-tech plans for Neom can only become reality with the use of artificial intelligence. The most cutting-edge achievements in AI will provide residents of the city with autonomous vehicles, public safety and crime prevention, error-free medicine, inclusive education, fast drone delivery, 3D printing, smart homes and many other systems designed to make Neom and other cities of the future the most modern and efficient smart urban developments of the new era.

Smart cities

AI in the oil and gas industry

The introduction of smart technologies promises significant price shifts in world energy markets. While today developing economies benefit from their cheaper labor costs, the rapid progress of new AI solutions can change the balance of power in favor of automated production in developed countries.

With their widespread digital literacy and good overall levels of well-being, developed economies will not find the quick reorientation of labor resources to higher-tech industries to be difficult. A similar redistribution in global energy markets will also be reflected in changing flows of investment, putting developing economies in an even more vulnerable position because of their diminishing competitive advantages.

The oil and gas industry remains one of the key drivers of economic growth in Kazakhstan and, of course, will continue to play a leading role in the development of the country. Therefore, it is equally important to know how artificial intelligence influences the value chain in this industry.

The oil and gas industry is divided into three main operating sectors: upstream, midstream and downstream. Upstream includes site exploration and the extraction and production of oil and natural gas. Midstream usually refers to the stages of transportation and storage. Downstream covers a variety of processes associated with refining and selling oil. Artificial intelligence is being introduced by large companies at almost all levels, but is most notable at present in the most upstream function of all: geological exploration.

In recent years, the global oil giants have begun to actively introduce artificial intelligence applications in operational sectors. For example, Total Oil, together with Google Cloud, is working on an artificial intelligence system for analyzing subsoil data to improve exploration and production processes ("Total," 2018). Those processes include the mapping and analysis of seismic activity at potential oil fields. Traditionally, most of the data collected by the company, such as seismic records, was in the form of image files that geologists analyzed manually.

ExxonMobil is working with researchers at MIT to automate the process of hydrocarbon exploration through the joint development of deep-sea exploration robots. Professor Brian Williams and his team at the MIT Computer Science and Artificial Intelligence Laboratory (CSAIL) previously worked on NASA's Curiosity rover and developed software for artificial intelligence that helped the Mars rover actively explore the surface of that planet ("A Collaboration," 2016).

These robots are to be used to automate the natural process of detection. Traditionally, oil and gas companies have used teams of divers and geologists to study underwater anomalies. Now, the use of AI will help oil and gas companies to reduce costs and delays in exploration.

GE's Baker Hughes Field Maintenance Service is also using NVIDIA-based artificial intelligence analysis of seismic, well log, sensor data and supply chain data (Paikeday, 2018).

The Industrial Internet of Things (IIoT) is actively used in the oil and gas industry, attracting large investors. In 2017, SoftBank invested about $400 million in the American company OSIsoft, which specializes in artificial intelligence and predictive analytics. OSlsoft developed predictive IoT software for power plants, which immediately attracted shipping and energy companies, especially in the oil and gas, water and mining industries (Baker, 2017).

In September 2018, Shell Global Solutions announced a partnership with Microsoft to accelerate the industry's transformation in both its upstream and downstream enterprises. Under this agreement, Shell uses Microsoft Azure's C3 IoT software platform to increase its efficiency in all sectors, from drilling and production to employee security. The oil giant predicts that using AI applications and machine learning will improve its operational performance (Husseini, 2018).

In January 2019, British Petroleum invested £5 million in the start-up Belmont Technology, which is to create the AI "Sandy Cloud" geoscience platform to interpret geological, geophysical, historical and project data for each reservoir. In this case, the AI uses neural networks to model and interpret results (Ali, 2019a).

In March 2019, the UK Oil and Gas Authority launched the country's first National Oil and Gas Data Repository (NDR).[56] It contains 130 terabytes of geophysical, infrastructural, field and well data, which is equivalent to about eight years of HD video. This data covers more than 12,500 wells, 5,000 seismic surveys and 3,000 pipelines. As a result, NDR provides companies with access to a huge pool of data, freeing them from regulatory requirements for information storage (Ali, 2019b).

AI can also be used to increase the security of operations on oil and gas platforms. In March 2019, Aker Solutions entered into a partnership agreement with the technology company SparkCognition to improve AI applications as part of its business's Cognitive Operation Initiatives ("SparkCognition," 2019). Its analytical solutions platform SparkPredict now controls installations on more than 30 marine structures. It uses machine learning algorithms to analyze the data coming in from sensors, which allow the company to identify non-optimal operations and impending failures before they occur.

The Russian company Gazprom Neft has been developing its own software products since 2012 to further goals for import substitution. As a result, the company has its own tools based on artificial intelligence technologies, including the ERA.OptimA program, which uses mathematical optimization algorithms to find the best solution for the development of hydrocarbon fields. The company also has tools for the earliest stages of exploration, for example to search for analogs of deposits: the machine helps to evaluate a deposit that has not been completely studied by comparing it with an analogous deposit that has already been drilled.[57]

Gazprom Neft has developed joint technologies with such companies as IBM, Yandex and Skoltech. A notable result was the June 2019 discovery of a new hydrocarbon reservoir by a self-learning program developed by Gazprom Neft together with IBM Services. Using both historical and incoming geological data, the neural network searches for patterns, determining where there is a chance of finding oil and gas-bearing strata not previously identified due to small size or complex geological structure. The program produces highly accurate predictions of the location of deposits that are not easy to detect by traditional methods. Work on data processing and the search for additional reserves at the field takes no more than a month. During a pilot project, the program was able to study data on more than 3000 wells in the field and suggest new layers of mineral deposits.[58] The presence of hydrocarbons in the designated formations was confirmed by industrial robots. As a result of the test, an influx of oil was obtained without building additional infrastructure.

These and other examples show that large companies around the world are making serious investments in promising AI initiatives for the oil and gas industry (Schlecht, 2017). Oil companies can save millions of dollars by minimizing unplanned downtime and production losses with AI. According to the Sloan Management Review, an average company producing liquefied natural gas reports five days of losses annually worth $125 million to $150 million. For an offshore platform, time losses can mean an average of $7 million per day. In periods of low energy prices, reducing operating costs is crucial.

In midstream sectors, companies can use AI to optimize transportation operations, including pipeline and secondary logistics. For example, AI can help improve maintenance intervals and pipeline inspections by analyzing and predicting corrosion levels in combination with environmental and operational information. Drones can be used to collect pipeline data.

Finally, downstream, analytical technologies and AI increase the availability of data and information, thereby contributing to the promotion of goods in pre-sale, sales and post-sale activities. Self-learning algorithms can analyze data much more thoroughly than people and significantly transform the entire oil and gas industry (Schlecht, 2017).

AI in the oil and gas industry

Social-credit rating

Artificial intelligence is quickly becoming a widely used competitive tool. Clearly, companies are no longer debating the pros and cons of AI, and have begun to introduce it in a massive way. In a survey conducted by McKinsey in 2018, 47% of respondents said their organizations had implemented at least one AI technology, and another 30% said they were in the process of piloting AI (Chui, 2018).

Artificial intelligence can help businesses in a wide range of areas, from customer support to personalization. AI can be used to:

1) improve customer service—for example, by using virtual assistants to provide real-time user support;

2) automate workloads—collecting and analyzing data from smart sensors or using machine learning algorithms to classify work and automatically route requests;

3) optimize logistics—for example, by using special algorithms to monitor infrastructure loads and plan traffic routes;

4) increase productivity and efficiency—for example, by automating a production line by integrating trainable industrial robots into processes;

5) predict productivity—using the IIoT and deep analytics of load and depreciation of production capacity;

6) increase the efficiency of interaction with customers—for example, by implementing imaging and voice processing systems that will help avoid queues and improve time statistics for customer service;

7) improve marketing—for example, by effectively tracking consumer behavior and preferences, as well as automating many routine marketing tasks.

Obviously, in the next ten years, artificial intelligence will transform ordinary economic processes and will significantly affect industries such as finance, manufacturing, transport, logistics, medicine and education.

McKinsey Global Institute researchers, in their article "Notes from the AI Frontier: Modeling the Influence of AI on the World Economy" (McKinsey, 2018b), estimate that artificial intelligence can potentially provide an additional economic effect of about $13 trillion by 2030, stimulating global GDP growth of 16%, or about 1.2% per year. The impact of AI may not be linear, as it may begin to accelerate with time. The contribution of AI to economic growth may be three or more times higher than in the next five years by 2030, due to the cumulative effect of competition and the discovery of additional new opportunities.

PricewaterhouseCoopers makes even more optimistic forecasts. Their study (PWC, 2017) shows that by 2030, as a result of AI, the global economy could grow to $15.7 trillion. Of this, more than 40% will be attributable to an increase in productivity, and the rest to consumption. This is due to the fact that over time, AI will increase the range and availability of personalized products.

If such predictions become a reality, the effect of AI will be comparable to the impact of other innovative technologies in their time, such as the discovery of electricity (Burgess, 2018).

In China, the idea of a Social Credit Rating[59] introduces a completely new understanding of the use of financial data to generate credit ratings for individuals, as well as companies, on a national scale. Despite the name, the system has nothing to do with the social welfare system; on the contrary, it is a system of economic transactions aimed at improving the market environment, and reducing transaction costs and economic risks.

Kazakhstan's eastern neighbor began to create this system in 2010 as a pilot program (Pisarenko, 2019), and it officially began construction of a nationwide system of social credit in 2014. Currently, individual elements of the system are in beta testing in 40 cities of the country.

Progress is already apparent. By 2020, every citizen of China will have access to a searchable file that contains all the data received from public and private companies to track his or her social credit (Minter, 2019). There are even plans to measure each citizen's points in real time.

The reason for creating such a large-scale digital economic system or "smart China" is as follows. The more developed a market economy, the more credit and loan operations take place, and the higher the degree of financial innovation, the more complex the structure of various credit products. The issue of credit risks becomes more acute, and the role of the credit system in general is even stronger.

In Western countries, thanks to their relatively well-developed legal framework, an advanced market economy, and an entrenched culture of loans, credit systems are mainly aimed at preventing and managing the risk of loan operations. All this produces a highly developed loan services sector, which enjoys broad trust. However, China, as its leaders admit, is still in a transitional stage of development towards a mature market system. But at the same time, it is a country which is technologically capable of maximizing the use of artificial intelligence.

It was "under AI" that China created a centralized, unified database of financial data on all loans in all sectors of the economy ("Planning," 2014). This included the collection and exchange of corporate credit information for assessing the creditworthiness of both companies and individuals. But the system is not limited to this; over time, all the information on all industries and the movement of goods and services will be embedded in it. This can be viewed as an independent segment in the business of tracking turnover based on product barcodes. However, it is also integrated with systems for quality control, taxes and income, and the movement of the workforce.

Naturally, when such a large-scale national platform is built, it can be used to solve many other problems. For example, it can identify low-income families, to provide them with welfare assistance and housing. The system as a whole also increases transparency in the academic environment, enhances transparency in the provision of public services, and ensures the solution of any tasks assigned to it.

With regard to the population, the capabilities of this artificial intelligence system look impressive, but at the same time quite ambiguous.

The Chinese authorities reasonably expect that by 2020, artificial intelligence will be able to recognize any resident of the country within three seconds. Other data, for example about a person's financial security, are actively integrated into the system. For example, the first data that should be subject to computer processing are data on the timeliness of payments for a person's taxes, loans, and so on. This is followed by information on traffic violations, disturbances to the public order, behavior on the internet and social networks, and compliance with social obligations. All this in aggregate can be used in a personal ranking system.

Social credit ratings can increase and decrease depending on a person's behavior. Buying diapers for a child can significantly increase your score, since the impersonal system assumes that you are a responsible caregiver. However, if you play video games for more than 10 hours a day, your social credit rating is likely to decline (Marr, 2019).

At the same time, a high social credit rating offers many advantages and privileges (Horsley, 2018). People with good scores receive various benefits: discounts on electricity, for example. They are offered the best deals by travel agencies. Individuals with a social credit score above 650 can receive free medical advice in hospitals.

Students receive additional social points for publishing scholarly papers, registering patents or volunteering. A social credit rating increased by such actions will reward them with significant benefits, from interviews with desirable employers and preferential access to rent apartments, to obtaining visas and buying online courses.

Not everyone considers the Chinese system to be safe and useful, rightly believing that the social credit rating system already prevents millions of Chinese citizens from moving freely around the country or traveling beyond its borders. In addition, no one can guarantee that the system cannot be hacked or used for illegal purposes. There are already precedents of such abuses. For example, according to a survey published in 2018, 946 residents of China were forbidden from flying for a whole year because of "inappropriate" behavior on airplanes. However, after a thorough investigation, it turned out that the overwhelming majority of the blacklisted travelers were people who had not paid their debts on time or had committed a traffic violation (Engelmann, 2018).

For many who live outside of China, this system of social credit rating seems based on a specifically Chinese model of contemporary socialism. But nothing in the technology limits its application to China alone; this system could be applied anywhere in the world, if permitted by local laws.

Social-credit rating

Supercorporations

"No sensible decision can be made any longer without taking into account not only the world as it is, but the world as it will be."

Isaac Asimov

US Tech Giants: Microsoft, Google and Facebook

In 1996, when the US Congress made its first attempt to regulate the internet, one response was a new "Declaration of the Independence of Cyberspace" (Barlow, 1996), addressed to the governments of all developed countries of the world. It reads, in part, as follows:

"I come from Cyberspace, the new home of Mind. On behalf of the future, I ask you of the past to leave us alone. You are not welcome among us. You have no sovereignty where we gather. We have no elected government, nor are we likely to have one... You have no moral right to rule us nor do you possess any methods of enforcement we have true reason to fear. ... Cyberspace does not lie within your borders. ... We are creating a world that all may enter without privilege or prejudice accorded by race, economic power, military force, or station of birth."

Since 1969, when one computer was first connected to another, information technologies have gone through three major stages of development. The very first of these stages can be described as a period of decentralized innovation, when many inventions were implemented in adherence with open source principles.

But in the second stage, the commercial benefits of the use of information technology were discovered, and that prompted the commercialization and regulation of research and development. Subsequently, that led to the birth of monopolies. The very first of them was Microsoft, with its operating system Windows, which it connected with its Internet Explorer browser.

Twenty years later, with the birth of online search engines and online trading platforms, new monopolies and duopolies emerged, such as Amazon, eBay, and Alphabet. It took these companies very little time to turn into successful corporations. Today Google processes 40,000 requests per second, 3.5 billion searches per day and 1.2 trillion requests per year from all over the world.[60]

Selling digital advertising opened the floodgates to inflows of cash, and the new monopolies used some of the money to develop in new directions, to provide new services and start new businesses: Google started to launch services such as Gmail, the Chrome browser, the Android operating system for handheld devices, the Google Earth digital globe, Google Analytics for web activity analysis, YouTube for video hosting, Waze navigation, and finally the DeepMind artificial intelligence project.

The third stage of development began in the mid-2000s with the world's most successful social network, Facebook. Its original mission was "to make the world more open and connected."[61] To do so, the company opened its social network to the entire world, regardless of its users' nationalities, languages or individual interests. Moreover, Facebook users could embed their own designs and applications into the platform. With such features, the company attracted a huge number of users in a short period of time, growing from 100 million in 2008 to 1 billion by 2012 and 2.4 billion by the end of the first quarter of 2019.[62] This number becomes even higher if we add the one billion users of Instagram[63] and 500 million users of WhatsApp, [64] both now part of Facebook corporation.

These numbers are truly impressive. But the real question is not the number of users, but the ability to influence people using AI technologies. Against the background of recent discoveries in behavioral science and psychology, today personal data includes not only someone's name, age, and social contacts, but also their preferences, which we report ourselves with one click of the "like" button. In the current environment, when there are no clear legal rules restricting the in-depth analysis of open data, technology leaders have a green light to continue to improve methods of manipulating people's attitudes, inclining them towards particular consumer choices.

Amazingly, the supercorporations do not hide that they have that potential. It is clearly reflected in the following statement: "Google helps people find the goods they want to buy, and Facebook helps them decide what they want to buy" (Kirkpatrick, 2011). Their influence and capacities keep growing every day; they expand from one sphere to another. They will clearly continue to grow. It is hard to imagine our world without the products and services of the businesses mentioned at the start of this chapter. Six of the eight wealthiest people on the planet today are the founders of tech companies who built their wealth on computer software, telecommunications, online commerce, social networks and business analytics ("10 bogateishikh," 2019).

Combined, you have a picture of our world tomorrow, forever dominated on a global scale by a handful of technology supercorporations. And, as we can see from recent years' experience, the same companies are also the current leaders in development and implementation of artificial intelligence systems. The transition to smart technologies provides them with a new distribution market, and at the same time, with unprecedented opportunities to collect massive information about their users.

With the advent of a new era of artificial intelligence, previous economic and political systems must undergo drastic change willingly or not, deliberately or by default. This is the era when consumers will get customized services from Google, Amazon and other supercorporations. In their call centers they will use robots. In their 3D "print shops" they will be able to print anything on a 3D printer, including, one day, human organs for transplant. And your virtual assistant, supplied by a global computer network, will do your scheduling for work and leisure.

One potential outcome of this trend is to establish intelligent monitoring systems that will not only possess information on people's preferences and activities but also successfully predict behavior and, further, actually shape desires and intentions in consumers around the globe. And because the internet today has no borders, some corporations and states can interfere via AI methods in other countries' affairs, using the information space, software and hardware. Instances of such political manipulations achieved with AI capabilities, in an environment of growing geopolitical tensions, could lead to drastic access restrictions or even the complete shutdown of cyberspace within individual countries.

Digital isolation, voluntary or compulsory, could further divide the world community. And it is possible that in the near future we will witness the launch and operation of several national internet systems cut off from the global internet. The national segmentation of the internet could turn it into a repository of redundant data sufficient to control absolutely every individual user.

We can see the foundations of such future scenarios in what is already happening today.

Unexpected side of AI: Cambridge Analytica and Facebook

The Universal Declaration of Human Rights of 1948 proclaims that everyone is entitled to freedom of choice in their political, religious and other beliefs and opinions, as well as to the right to personal security. But the scandal generated by Cambridge Analytica's use of personal information in Facebook accounts, both for the benefit of Donald Trump's political campaign and during the Brexit referendum, revealed an unexpected side of the global opportunities and challenges of the era of artificial intelligence.

Today's social networks create the largest marketplace in the world, one with huge potential for the use of artificial intelligence, from face recognition to personality profiling. For example, they provide an opportunity to process information about all the objects in personal photos and their correlations. If a social network user keeps posting photos in which he appears next to motorcycles of different models, receiving numerous likes and positive comments, it is obvious that this user is a potential buyer of two-wheeled motor vehicles. He will immediately start to receive contextual advertising about motorcycles and all that goes with them. And because no human deliberation is involved, it only takes a second or two for the AI to identify such correlations and target sales messages accordingly.

Developers of social networks study the social connections, interests and hobbies of their users not only for the purpose of targeting advertising, but also to keep users active. Even if a new Facebook user, after registering, does not publish any personal information about himself, the social network will still find people the user may know. A potential circle of friends can be easily rated by likes, geodata, photos and other information.

Moreover, Facebook now has new cards in its hands: WhatsApp and Instagram, both of which it owns. Therefore, it is very likely that the new Facebook user will be asked to add his contacts from other applications to his friends list. Chats in messengers can be assessed for activity level and mood, without even touching on the topics of conversations. This will help filter the list of recommended friends, offering the user only those with whom he most prefers to communicate.

With full understanding of these opportunities, in 2014, the company Cambridge Analytica used the Facebook database to develop a system that could personalize political advertising. According to journalists from Guardian Media Group, Cambridge Analytica obtained more than 50 million profiles of Facebook users to create a powerful program that would predict and influence voting results (Cadwalladr, 2018).

Users' data was collected through an app called thisisyourdigitallife, created by Aleksandr Kogan, a research associate at Cambridge Analytica. For this app, users were paid to take a personality assessment test and agreed to have their data collected for academic use.

However, the Cambridge Analytica app did not only collect information about whether the user passed that test, but also about his friends on Facebook, even though the company was aware that Facebook had a policy banning the collection of data on app users' friends except for specific purposes (and not for sale or advertising). This led to the accumulation of a huge database of information about tens of millions of people. And this database, which includes 50 million individual profiles which could be matched to electoral lists, was transferred to a third party. These data were very valuable because they could identify personality types and predict the political preferences of voters during elections.

Naturally, throughout this process, powerful AI capabilities were used. A special algorithm in combination with the database led to the creation of an unprecedented political tool. This event was one of the first and largest violations of cyberspace laws in modern history. Moreover, the illegal use of personal information would have remained hidden from the world if it were not for the investigation conducted by the Guardian Media Group journalists, as well as the testimony of Canadian experts Christopher Wiley and Brittany Kaiser, who had previously worked for Cambridge Analytica. It was they who revealed the critical information on the company's work in influencing the elections prior to their 2016 intrusion in the US elections, in various African countries, Malaysia, and also in the UK in the Brexit referendum ("Great Hack," 2019).

When the scandal became public, Facebook deleted the app and suspended Cambridge Analytica from the platform. But investigations triggered by the huge public outcry over the revelations continue to this day. Worse, new instances of Facebook information being used to extract personal data to predict behavioral patterns keep emerging. In 2019 Facebook even filed a lawsuit in California against the Rankwave company, a Cambridge Analytica analogue in South Korea.

The Cambridge Analytica scandal shows us that AI-processed data can serve as an excellent tool to manipulate the preferences of human populations. And there is reason to believe that the amounts of digitized information generated by each person will keep growing, while cognitive analysis methods will keep improving.

The Cambridge Analytica and Facebook scandal revealed an unexpected side of the global opportunities and challenges of the new era of artificial intelligence. They require serious thought. The roles played by the states and the global community in cyberspace and digital privacy regulation have become very clearly defined. In the era of total digitization, the conceptualization of new fundamental and undeniable human rights becomes more urgent than ever.

Chinese Tech Giants: Alibaba, Baidu, Huawei and Tencent

The year 2019 was marked by dramatic events centered on Huawei,[65] including the imposition of sanctions by the United States and the arrest of a very high-ranking official ("SShA vnesli," 2019). In mid-May 2019, the US government imposed restrictions on the supply of components and technology to Huawei, which resulted in the termination of all cooperation with the company by US and UK corporations, and in particular Google, on whose operating system (Android) Huawei phones work, and ARM, which provides key components of the integrated circuits used in all Huawei products.

On the one hand, the Chinese corporation was accused of espionage and of violating sanctions on third parties, notably Iran. Against the backdrop of the wide-ranging revelations about Huawei's misconduct, several major European and Japanese companies have also suspended their partnerships with it. But of course, in an era of tightly bound global value chains, trade wars create difficulties for all parties, and not only for the company that falls under the restrictions.

In the case at hand, Huawei is the world's largest manufacturer of equipment for the introduction of 5G technology, and one of the world's leading manufacturers of smartphones, which automatically means the existence of multi-billion-dollar contracts with companies around the world.

Inevitably the restrictions imposed on Huawei have seriously hurt some American companies for whom the Chinese technology giant is an extremely valuable client (McBride, 2019). Google alone, the first to suspend cooperation with Huawei, is set to lose up to 800 million Android users, according to its president, implying significant losses.[66] But of course there are also beneficiaries: the European corporations Ericsson and Nokia, Huawei's main competitors in the 5G technology market, have significantly strengthened their positions. Considering the enormous potential of 5G wireless communications, which will eventually be a thousand times faster than the current 4G, primacy in this market is an extremely valuable asset. This technology breaks down the current standards of hardware and telecommunications support, because really big data can be transmitted wirelessly.

In the sanctions fight against Huawei, a thaw began quickly, after American technology makers prompted the US leadership to lift at least some restrictions. But this episode perfectly demonstrates the ongoing battle for primacy in the promising technologies of tomorrow.

Huawei is not the only Chinese corporation that actively promotes its role in the global innovation market. For example, Baidu, a search company valued at $191 billion, has filed 2,368 patent applications in the field of AI, particularly in the areas of natural language processing, intelligent search, speech recognition and driverless vehicles (Shead, 2018). No other IT company has filed as many applications.

WeChat, the most popular instant messaging app in China (it is owned by Tencent[67]), was started in 2011, a mere eight years ago, but it already has almost a billion users. The scale of the services offered by this company exceeds even those of Facebook, Messenger and WhatsApp, because aside from text messaging, WeChat can also be used to make payments, order goods and services, and transfer funds between contacts, thus functioning as an e-wallet. WeChat's success is so huge that other technology companies in China, such as Alipay from the Alibaba Group,[68] are also offering e-wallets.

Not surprisingly, Tencent is actively developing artificial intelligence technologies. The corporation's laboratories conduct research in machine learning, speech recognition, natural language processing, computer vision, image analysis and robotics. They also develop practical AI applications for businesses, including online games, social networking and cloud services.

Today, Alibaba is one of the major investors in the implementation of AI applications in the Chinese economy, and it is involved in creating a national cloud storage system, which aims to integrate all sectors of the country's economy by 2020. The list of AI technologies created by the company includes chatbots for retailers and customers, smart city technologies, apps for the aviation, agriculture and hospitality industries and much more. For example, the Dian Xiaomi chatbot understands more than 90% of Alibaba customers' requests and serves more than 3.5 million users per day, while the City Brain in Hangzhou generates and processes all city data in the cloud (Marr, 2018b). Today, Alibaba is present in almost all sectors of the Chinese economy, and is striving to broaden its presence in other parts of the world.

Supernations

"I do not know with what weapons World War III will be fought, but World War IV will be fought with sticks and stones."

Albert Einstein

Leaders and strategies: The US and China

Today, artificial intelligence has become a new factor in the global competition for power. Indeed, the development of AI is beginning to emerge as a major tool for the enhancement of overall national economic competitiveness, and of national security.

More and more countries (over thirty by now) are joining the race to develop AI, but the technology leaders have already been decided: the United States and China. Their strengths are very different, with the US far ahead in the development of the underlying technologies, and China ahead in applying them. It is those two countries that dominate today's market for venture capital and direct equity investments in the field of AI. The United States is in first place, accounting for 70-80% of global VC investments in all types of technology. China ranks second: in 2017, its companies attracted 36% of global private investment in the AI sector (OECD, 2018). If this continues, they will be the only two countries able to skim the cream off AI's future benefits.

According to experts at PWC, as a result of the introduction of AI, China's GDP growth from 2019 to 2030 will be 26.1%, while the US economy will add 14.5% (PWC, 2018a). Together, the two countries will account for about 70% of the total impact of AI on the global economy.

In the US, the introduction of more productive AI-enabled technologies will provide very large opportunities for GDP growth. The benefits will be accelerated because of the high degree of technological and consumer readiness for AI, as well as the impact of the rapid accumulation of assets allowed by ever-increasing points of contact between data flows.

China is rapidly catching up with the US in introducing AI systems, which is having a broad impact on its (growing) labor productivity. A key part of the country's potential is the great availability of reinvestment capital in the domestic economy, as compared with the countries of Europe and North America. Chinese enterprises are more actively using their profits to expand their AI capabilities and derive profits from them (PWC, 2017).

The Chinese AI plan adopted in July 2017 attracted much attention from the international community because of its explicitly expressed global ambitions. In the officially approved "Next Generation Artificial Intelligence Development Plan," China announced its intention to become the world leader in the field of research, technological development and the use of artificial intelligence.

The Chinese government pays considerable attention to machine learning techniques that require large amounts of data. One of the main drivers is the capacity of the domestic market of China, which has the largest number of internet users in the world and, therefore, the largest array of data for developments in the field of AI, actively being used by the market leaders Baidu, Alibaba and Tencent.

China still lags behind the US in certain technical areas such as IT hardware, the development of algorithms, and the creation of commercial AI ecosystems ("Razvitie," 2019). However, China holds some positions that will allow it to become the undisputed leader of the global AI market in the very near future.

Why is China's success in the field of artificial intelligence inevitable?

In his book *AI Superpowers: China, Silicon Valley and the New World Order* (Lee, 2018), author Kai-fu Lee—a leading AI expert, former president of Google China, and now a prominent investor in AI technology—offers some valid arguments for China's future AI leadership.

According to Lee, the country certainly has enormous scale for data accumulation. If data is indeed the main resource for AI development, then China is many times ahead of any other country in the world. Various sources state that more than 800 million Chinese people use the internet,[69] and the country is home to more than 700 million smartphone owners[70] and almost 200 million surveillance cameras (Mozur, 2018). China beats the United States and Europe combined in all these statistics.

As a significant advantage, the author also notes strong support from the government, which contributed to the adoption of almost 800 AI programs for the development of the industry and the construction of sixty AI industrial parks. The Chinese government actively supports the massive introduction of innovations and is building all the necessary infrastructure.

Another important advantage is the high degree of public readiness for the introduction of AI applications, as evidenced by the country's leadership in publications, as well as the active dissemination of AI technologies in the public sector and their implementation in infrastructure. Lee claims that the Chinese public is far more relaxed about privacy than westerners are, which is also an essential factor in the AI race.

Finally, Lee writes, the Chinese business model is well suited to rolling out the benefits of AI across the economy. Unlike Western companies that take a safety-conscious approach, Chinese companies live by the principle of "move fast and break things", which gives them a significant head start in a hypercompetitive environment.

Against this background, China's attraction of 60% of the money invested in AI around the world over the past five years is unsurprising ("China AI Development," 2018). This allows the economy to set the ambitious goal of becoming the world leader in the field of AI technology. The State Council of the People's Republic of China officially proclaimed that by 2025, AI will become "the main driving force behind industrial modernization and economic transformation in China." By 2030, the market size of AI technologies should be more than 1 trillion yuan ($147 billion), with related sectors worth 10 trillion yuan ($1.5 trillion). Thus, the AI industry in this country will be at the top of the high value added chain. And by 2030, Chinese research, technological development and the use of artificial intelligence are expected to go global, turning China into the main global center of innovation.

With the help of AI, the Chinese government aims not only to increase national competitiveness, but also to strengthen the country's defenses and guarantee its internal security. According to the plan, AI will be used to create intelligent monitoring systems, to preclude or at least contain potential threats.

Because China is still in the process of strengthening its AI capacity, the country's national plan calls for the use of "international innovation resources." This means that the Chinese government encourages international cooperation in the field of AI, including buy-ins through mergers and acquisitions, investments in equity and venture capital, as well as the establishment of research and development centers abroad. All are now being impeded by increasing restrictions imposed in the US and other countries, but in the long term, as its own capacities develop, China will become less dependent on foreign resources for innovation.

It is no coincidence that the Chinese government declared its intention to open a network of the most advanced global centers of innovation and training in the field of AI by 2030. The current deficit in basic research will be reversed by investments in long-term innovation.

The Chinese government and the country's leading AI companies are now prioritizing the selection and training of AI specialists. This is considered to be the most important competitive factor. Among a number of programs for the recruitment and training of leading experts, the Thousand Talents project has attracted particular attention, because it is designed to attract foreign scientists and IT engineers, as well as to encourage Chinese scientists to work on their research exclusively in China.

In order to strengthen its human resources pool, the government of China is devoting much attention to improving education and training in the field of AI. This will soon lead to the institutionalization of AI as a new field of study, with its own university departments and research institutions, to accommodate programs for undergraduates as well as for master's and doctoral students. In addition, the introduction of new higher education and vocational programs across the board will help prepare China's labor force for a new job market shaped by the ever-wider use of artificial intelligence.

The Chinese government is aware of the fact that with the expansion of AI, new risks and challenges will arise for economic security and social stability. And its plan is aimed at minimizing such risks to ensure that AI develops in a way that is safe, reliable and controlled. The plan provides for the drafting of laws, regulations and ethical standards relating to artificial intelligence, as well as rules and mechanisms for security and supervision. Moreover, China does not hide the fact that it seeks to achieve international influence through the development and implementation of global AI standards.

The government also seeks to ensure a better quality of life for its people through the use of AI in agriculture, in the transportation industry, in the social security and pension system, and in public security and other government functions ("Next Generation," 2017). Interaction with the public will mainly be carried out using microblogging and Tencent's ubiquitous platform WeChat.

As China adopts its national plan for the development of AI, there have been calls for the development of similar plans in the US. In February 2019, the Trump administration issued a new order to create a national strategy for AI,[71] which aims to promote scientific discovery, economic competitiveness and national security. The initiative is to be coordinated through the US National Science and Technology Council's Special Committee on Artificial Intelligence.

It should be noted that Silicon Valley and the US Department of Defense have already begun initiatives to use artificial intelligence in the military sphere (Metz, 2018). In particular, new agencies have been created that make selective investments in companies developing military technologies using AI. Both the Pentagon and the CIA have vast financial and organizational resources at their disposal. At the end of June 2018, the US Department of Defense announced the creation of the Joint Center for Artificial Intelligence, the JAIC ("Memorandum," 2018).

The US government now seeks to encourage the development of appropriate technical standards and to reduce barriers to the safe testing and implementation of AI technologies. The goal is to ensure accelerated introduction of AI into existing sectors of the economy, as well as to create fundamentally new market segments based on AI. For example, the United States plans to expand access to high quality and fully traceable federal data, models and computing resources to increase their value and applicability in new research and development, but with consistent state support for security measures and privacy protection.

As in the Chinese plan, the US administration pays special attention to teaching current and future generations in the American workforce to use AI technologies so that they are ready for the reality of the near economic future. The United States also intends to strengthen public confidence in AI technologies while protecting the relevant civil rights.

At the same time, the US government is focusing increasingly on protecting critical AI technologies against their acquisition by strategic competitors. Thus at the end of 2018, Donald Trump ordered the US Foreign Investment Committee to monitor and block the acquisition of shares in US start-up companies by foreign countries. For similar reasons, the US Department of Commerce decided to include the Chinese telecommunications equipment manufacturer Huawei, along with 70 related companies, on its blacklist for "activities contrary to US national security" ("SShA vnesli," 2019). Such government actions illustrate the fierce competition between the two world powers in developing AI technologies.

AI pioneers: The strategies of Singapore and the UAE

In studying the experience of other countries, it is also important to consider how relatively small countries, such as Singapore and the UAE, have developed AI strategies. Those two countries are pioneers not only in planning, but also in implementing national strategies for artificial intelligence. Studying their experiences can increase our understanding of how Kazakhstan can develop its own path to AI.

In 2017, Singapore launched the AI Singapore program, worth $150 million over five years,[72] focused on investing in the next wave of AI. The program brings together all of Singapore's research institutes in a dynamic ecosystem of start-ups and companies that are developing AI products, in order to create tools and develop talent in order to solve some of the country's specific social and economic problems, and to expand the adoption of AI in national industries.

AI Singapore consists of four key initiatives. First, the Foundation for Basic Research will contribute to the development of the program as a whole. Second, the "Grand Challenges" initiative supports the work of interdisciplinary teams that provide innovative solutions to topical issues faced by Singapore and the rest of the world. It currently focuses on healthcare, urban solutions and finance. Third is the initiative "100 Experiments," aimed at solving the problems of AI in industry, and providing assistance for the creation of AI teams. Finally, the fourth initiative is the "AI Apprenticeship," a nine-month structured program aimed at preparing a new cohort of talent in the field of AI, by increasing technical specialization and skills. The program involves a two-month in-depth course on machine learning, and then a seven-month practical training period to tackle specific assignments.

In Singapore, a number of industries are already actively using AI solutions, including the health care sector. AI instruments can detect skin cancer, analyze chest X-rays, and screen for diabetes with retinal scans. Scientists from the Genome Institute of Singapore (GIS) have developed a new type of AI, based on computer models and machine learning, to accurately identify the underlying causes of gastric cancer. The AI methods and technologies developed in the framework of this study will help researchers understand the effect of mutations in non-coding DNA in other types of cancer.

Another successful AI development effort is in transportation, with a focus on the development of autonomous vehicles. The new facilitating legislation enacted in 2018 attracted worldwide attention and made Singapore a testing ground for this innovative mode of transportation.

In 2015, the automotive company nuTonomy, which develops software for autonomous vehicles and mobile robots, began testing autonomous vehicles in Singapore. It established partnerships with the country's most popular car-sharing service, Grab, to increase the availability of autonomous taxis. However, until this type of vehicle is considered completely safe, all taxis will still have a driver in case of an emergency.

Initiatives are currently being taken to develop autonomous buses and to explore how this technology can be used for freight transport. Interestingly, instead of creating autonomous vehicles, nuTonomy tries to integrate its technology with existing vehicles and thus speed up the implementation process.

Singapore is also actively implementing AI solutions in the world of finance and business. For example, to improve the quality of customer service, financial services use facial recognition technology, which optimizes the verification process and, consequently, speeds up credit processes.

Like other countries of the world, Singapore seeks to address the shortage of AI-qualified personnel with various educational initiatives. The AI Singapore program will train 12,000 industry professionals and students to develop a local cohort of experts with artificial intelligence skills (Lago, 2019). At present, more than 3,000 professionals have completed this training.

Universities in Singapore play an important role in implementing the strategy, helping the country in its struggle for leadership in the field of AI. According to the world education rankings in the Times Higher Education magazine, Nanyang Technological University (NTU) ranks third in the world in AI research after the Massachusetts Institute of Technology and Carnegie Mellon University (Tham, 2019).

In June 2018, AI Singapore established the Advisory Council on the Ethical Use of AI and Data, which supports the ethical and responsible implementation and use of AI-based technologies. The government believes it is imperative to build trust in AI and other digital technologies to facilitate their adoption. The Advisory Council launched a research program on the management of AI and data, which deals with legal, regulatory, ethical and political issues related to data protection and the use of AI.

In January 2019, the Advisory Board released the first voluntary model for managing AI in Asia. The framework provides a "people-centered approach," meaning that AI should be used to empower people, not to put them at risk. When developing and using AI, the first rule should be to ensure the protection of human interests.

In 2017, the government of the United Arab Emirates (UAE) also launched an Artificial Intelligence Strategy to improve labor efficiency and increase economic growth, and resolved to become a key investor in the field of AI by 2031. The UAE was also the first country in the world to create a Ministry of Artificial Intelligence, which is responsible for implementing the overall strategy and funding various projects. The AI strategy in the UAE is meant to reduce government spending, diversify the economy and position the country as a world leader in the field.

This AI strategy covers almost all sectors of the economy, including health care, renewable energy, water and traffic. In the transportation sector, the strategy is aimed at reducing accidents and operating costs, as well as optimizing traffic flows. In the health sector, the government intends to minimize the occurrence of chronic diseases. The important problem of water supply for the country is also to be tackled with in-depth analysis and research using AI. By 2031, the UAE also plans to fully integrate current AI capabilities into its medical and security services.

Its government created the first World Council on artificial intelligence.

The strategy provides for five main areas of implementation. First, the creation of the Council on AI, mentioned above. Second, numerous seminars, educational programs and other initiatives to train public servants in the field of AI. Third, the strategy plans to develop the abilities and skills of all employees working in the field of AI technologies. The fourth area of the strategy is the introduction and integration of AI into operations at all medical institutions and in the security services. And the last prong of their efforts involves launching a leadership strategy and issuing laws governing the safe use of AI.

The UAE has invested heavily in creating an accessible ecosystem for companies that are committed to AI. By 2030, the sector is expected to increase the country's GDP by about 14%, equivalent to $96 billion (PWC, 2018a).

The country's government is also actively investing in training its citizens in artificial intelligence technologies. Students are trained under an agreement signed between Oracle and local technology colleges to prepare young citizens of the UAE for future work with AI.

The construction and transportation sectors are introducing AI in national road projects, which is intended to reduce implementation time by 54%, fuel consumption by 37%, labor dependence by 80% and equipment usage by 40%.

On April 22, 2019, the "National Strategy of Artificial Intelligence 2031" was adopted. As part of this new strategy, an AI innovations incubator and the "Academy of AI" were created, and funds were designated for attracting and training AI talent and expanding research potential. The plan also includes "creating a brand of artificial intelligence in the UAE."

According to official forecasts, by 2035, AI will add $182 billion to the national economy. Along those lines, in the period from 2015 to 2018, Dubai attracted $21 billion in foreign investment in AI and robotics. The authorities have taken key initiatives to ensure the implementation of the strategy.

Dubai and Abu Dhabi have developed a special policy to further strengthen the position of AI in the UAE at the local level. Abu Dhabi has created a unique global technology ecosystem called "HUB 71" in a collaboration with Microsoft and SoftBank, with the support of the Abu Dhabi Investment Office. This ecosystem combines three unique factors for success: access to capital, business partners and strategic partners, all in one place.

The Abu Dhabi municipal government also created a fund in the amount of $13.6 billion, called "Ghadan 21," which finances high-tech projects and companies in such promising areas as AI and IoT. New York University in Abu Dhabi currently has StartAD, a platform for entrepreneurs that began accepting applications from AI and IoT start-ups in 2018.

In 2018, the city of Dubai launched the "Smart Dubai 2021" strategy to turn Dubai into a smart city. The plan includes a detailed roadmap to achieve this goal. Smart Dubai 2021 has identified 100 key performance indicators. Exact goals were set in six dimensions: Smart Life, Smart Economy, Smart People, Smart Mobility, Smart Environment and Smart Management. A special office monitors the implementation of the development plan. Dubai also adopted a 3D printing strategy aimed at the construction, medical products and consumer goods sectors in order to build 25% of buildings in Dubai using 3D printing technology by 2030.

A new AI Camp has been created in the UAE. It is three months long and features classes conducted by engineers and managers from leading companies in the field of AI (Microsoft, IBM, etc.). The camp is free and funded by the Ministry of Artificial Intelligence. The program is aimed at attracting high school and university students, as well as government officials. In 2018, 5,000 students took advantage of various forms of related education.

The UAE is also developing and expanding existing rules: a team has been created to identify possible ethical principles for AI.

In April 2018, the UAE launched the Emirates Blockchain Strategy 2021. The ultimate goal is providing every citizen and resident of the UAE with a unique identification number for access to all of their personal documents and information within a secure system. Thanks to this innovation, the UAE hopes to improve security, as well as reduce operating costs and improve decision-making processes. Half of all government transactions (and other interactions) are to occur on the blockchain platform by 2021.

Moreover, the UAE has significantly changed its long-term visa system in order to attract talent and businesses, with a 10-year resident visa for investors and specialists, and a 5-year resident visa for talented students and entrepreneurs.

While both countries (the UAE and Singapore) are global innovators in the adoption of AI, the Singapore program is more focused on corporate solutions and is supported by its strong academic institutions. However, as a nation-city with limited growth opportunities, Singapore faces certain limitations in scale. Meanwhile the UAE, with a population twice as large as Singapore's and a territory a hundred times bigger, can implement an artificial intelligence strategy that is scalable in other jurisdictions.

AI pioneers: The strategies of Singapore and the UAE

AI and the Military

A key issue with military applications of artificial intelligence is the question of whether machines should be independent in making and implementing decisions. It is expected, or feared, that sooner or later, urgency will demand that decision-making in using weapons be delegated to artificial intelligence apps. Prospective AI applications range widely, from providing high-tech support to existing weapon systems, individual troop formations or individual soldiers to actually replacing those soldiers with combat robots.

At present, AI is being applied in the planning and/or control of reconnaissance, attack, defense, and logistics operations, as well as in command and control activities. For example, "smart vision" and augmented reality technologies, which allow the machine recognition of objects "seen" by optical or thermal imaging cameras, are already being used for the basic military intelligence task of scouting enemy forces and relevant terrain. Beyond that, there is already a fully operational robotic anti-radar unmanned aircraft (a.k.a. "loitering munition"), and a robotic llama that walks alongside foot soldiers to carry loads (replacing real llamas). And there is work in progress on robotic patrol vehicles, autonomous armored combat vehicles (much closer to realization than autonomous cars), and more experimentally, robot soldiers capable of simple tasks which need not be human-looking "androids."

By contrast, the use of artificial intelligence to aim short-range weapons and guide long-range weapons is imminent. It offers the possibility of minimizing civilian casualties while increasing the efficiency and cost-effectiveness of military operations. Moreover, autonomous weapon systems and de-mining devices promise to reduce military casualties.

The autonomous robots that are already in wide use are the unmanned aerial vehicles used by a number of countries for scouting and attack. In almost all cases, however, they are still guided by human beings for much of the time, and certainly when launching attacks. Earlier types had to be guided continuously because they were remotely piloted, rather than robotic. The first unmanned aerial vehicles were developed and deployed by Israel in the 1970s initially only for photo reconnaissance; now they are increasingly present in the armed forces of the US, China, Russia, Iran and other countries.

Autonomous methods are frequently used in air defense systems, to locate air targets more promptly and precisely and to destroy them, if necessary.

While the United States and China have focused, to a degree, on aerial systems, Russia has made significant advances in the use of autonomous vehicles on land, on the sea and underwater. The announcement of plans to produce the "Poseidon" unmanned submarine for the Russian Navy has motivated other countries to begin active research for similar vehicles. And Chinese as well as US forces have recently tested autonomous powerboats, mostly for coast guard duties.

But of course, the highest degree of autonomy has been achieved in space, where, for objective reasons, human participation in the functioning of various near-Earth and outer space systems is minimal.

Efforts to militarize space have increased in recent years, and they require the development of a variety of autonomous space vehicles.

Cyberspace has also been recently recognized as a new battleground. The armed forces of several countries (United States, Russia, China, the United Kingdom and Israel) include cyber units corps officially designated to block enemy cyberattacks, and launch cyber-offensives of their own.

The media has repeatedly published speculations or, perhaps, leaks about cyberattacks on critical components of enemy infrastructure, and about AI-enhanced propaganda aimed at both civilians and military personnel of opposing armies, as well as information gathering. But the question of whether cyberattacks are acts of military aggression that warrant military reprisals has not been resolved internationally.

Operationally, AI systems are already being used to identify enemy weaknesses, penetrate major systems and pick a perfect moment for causing the most damage. There are many ways to use artificial intelligence in military activities, but so far only a few are being pursued even by the United States and China, because as Tesla declared, there is no stomach for the large-scale replacement of extant military forces with AI-centered forces.

Nevertheless, strategic use of AI by the defense structures is evident even today. With the help of artificial intelligence systems, integrated command and control will be provided to minimize the time needed for decision-making and to achieve the greatest effect from the simultaneous use of the capabilities of air, naval and land forces enhanced by smart technologies. And yet again, the US and China are the leaders in this area: they invest enormous funds into "smart" developments in the military sector.

On February 12, 2019, the US Department of Defense announced its transition to a new strategy of artificial intelligence development, aimed at achieving superiority over other countries in this field (Cronk, 2019). This marks the start of a new stage in the perpetual arms race, based on smart technologies. The US Defense Department has already invested over $100 million in the development of what it calls "advanced" AI systems for military operations, while opening development centers.

One such center was opened at Carnegie Mellon University in Pittsburgh, Pennsylvania: a large integrated AI center run by the US Armed Forces, which also supervises high-potential programs for ground troops and developments in the field of military communications and electronics.

The United States is now a recognized leader in the development of unmanned aerial vehicles (UAVs), which use AI to automate all piloting functions, including targeting.

The Chinese government has announced plans to achieve world leadership in applying AI for military purposes, by 2030. For this purpose, state entities have been directed to import as much as $150 billion worth of assorted AI technology (Kharpal, 2017).

In pursuing AI applications, the Chinese method seems to be based on a simple decisions principle (yes or no), while the American approach to research relies upon deep learning and complex algorithms. What is certain is that Chinese entities have focused on the acquisition of technology with very little funding for basic research. Now that technology imports are increasingly restricted, entities such as Huawei will need to start at the beginning.

Russia is another country that is emphasizing the development of AI military technologies. According to information published in the media, by the end of 2019 Russia intends to release its road map for a national AI strategy (Bendett, 2019). Not long before that, in the fall of 2018, the military innovation technopolis known as Era was launched on Russia's Black Sea coast (Bendett, 2018). It is used for the development, testing and introduction of new types of weapons based on smart AI technologies, specifically autonomous vehicles, including autonomous submarines, hypersonic weapons, combat robots and other weapons of the 21st century.

South Korea is also looking very attentively at developing autonomous weapons. It already uses automated systems to target and destroy enemy troops in the Demilitarized Zone (DMZ) on its border with North Korea. In May of 2018, the Korean Ministry of National Defense announced its intention to replace some soldiers with combat robots, explaining this measure as a response to a demographic crisis.

Open-source data make it possible to follow the most important trends in the military use of AI. Trends in the development of technologies based on artificial intelligence indicate a striving to minimize the human component in decision-making processes, and exploit the unprecedented growth in computer systems' productive capabilities. In all simulations of armed conflicts, the winning side is always the one that uses AI abilities most efficiently. Taking advantage of extensive computing power, access to various autonomous combat vehicles and decision-making discretion when calculating how to defeat an enemy, AI will always be way ahead of any opposing side in tactics, strategy and efficient use of different means of destruction. The one who achieves the best results in independent decision-making processes will be the most effective.

High hopes are currently being placed on research in quantum computing systems. But it should be noted that those in charge of the biggest world powers' armed forces are still very wary of the prospect of delegating decision-making to AI methods. Because of that, most developments focus on automating the many processes that make it possible for people to control autonomous machines remotely. The central goal is to increase the number of machines that can be operated by one person, and to improve efficiency due to complementary tasks being performed by different robots.

The governments and peoples of most countries in the world have developed a significant aversion to the arms race in general and to the development of military AI systems in particular. It is quite obvious to all that life and death decisions cannot be delegated to artificial intelligence systems except in special circumstances (such as within the Korean DMZ). Nor can strategic decision-making be delegated in any significant way: errors or digital malfunctions that could trigger a large-scale military conflict with potentially global consequences cannot be controlled or limited; they can only be precluded by excluding AI from the actual chain of command.

Unfortunately, that is no guarantee that nobody will do it, in order to avoid the delays of human decision-making in a time-sensitive stand-off. And the history of war teaches that absolutely inhumane methods will be used under sufficient pressure, with the victorious side later calling them "forced measures." Examples of this include the use of chemical weapons during World War I and the use of nuclear weapons during World War II.

The problems associated with the risks of using AI in the military sector have been repeatedly voiced in various international forums and international organizations. In particular, several states have used the United Nations as a platform to raise the question of how to regulate and limit the use of military technologies based on artificial intelligence. However, they did not find support from the countries that are already involved in the AI arms race and are not willing to give up their priority in this field.

Those countries are ignoring the potential impact of AI systems in a situation in which a world war has been deliberately ignited, including a possible nuclear missile strike, and discounting the risks that military AI technologies could be used for terrorist purposes. Moreover, any further expansion in the gap in AI development between the world powers and other countries may lead to a further and dramatic stratification of the global community, with the real possibility of some countries coming to dominate over others in a way that may resemble a new kind of colonialism. The only way to avoid these and other negative phenomena is through negotiations and the creation of new associations of countries that support principles of mutual control in the development and use of AI systems for military and other purposes.

There may be no more pressing issue on today's global agenda than the need for international regulation of the military use of artificial intelligence. And individual methods and developments (for example, killer drones and the most harmful cyber programs) should be treated like weapons of mass destruction, with the appropriate restrictions or a complete moratorium applied.

AI and the Military

Flyorov and Einstein

In 1942, Georgy Flyorov, a Soviet nuclear physicist who is known for his discovery of spontaneous fission, sent a letter to Josef Stalin, to persuade him of the necessity to start an atomic bomb project in the USSR. In parts, his letter read as follows:[73]

"What makes the uranium projects fantastic are the enormous prospects that will open up if a successful solution to the problem is found... A veritable revolution will occur in military hardware. It may take place without our participation, simply due to the fact that now, as before, the scientific world is governed by sluggishness. In some areas of nuclear physics we managed to rise to the level of foreign scientists and even outrun them in some areas, but now we are making a big mistake voluntarily surrendering our positions."

At the time, with the German armies still advancing, the Soviet Union was in a dire situation, and the suggestion that millions of rubles should be spent on a project that could only produce results in ten, fifteen or even twenty years seemed far-fetched. Yet Flyorov's letter, at first overlooked, ultimately did lead to the launch of the Soviet nuclear project.

A similar event had happened earlier in the United States. In 1939, Albert Einstein signed a letter in which he asked the President Roosevelt to look into the potential of atomic bomb development. It reads as follows:

Sir:
Some recent work by E. Fermi and L. Szilard, which has been communicated to me in manuscript, leads me to expect that the element uranium may be turned into a new and

important source of energy in the immediate future. Certain aspects of the situation which has arisen seem to call for watchfulness and, if necessary, quick action on the part of the Administration. I believe therefore that it is my duty to bring to your attention the following facts and recommendations.

In the course of the last four months it has been made probable—through the work of Joliot in France as well as Fermi and Szilard in America—that it may be possible to set up a nuclear chain reaction in a large mass of uranium, by which vast amounts of power and large quantities of new radium-like elements would be generated. Now it appears almost certain that this could be achieved in the immediate future.

This new phenomenon would also lead to the construction of bombs, and it is conceivable—though much less certain—that extremely powerful bombs of this type may thus be constructed. A single bomb of this type, carried by boat and exploded in a port, might very well destroy the whole port together with some of the surrounding territory. However, such bombs might very well prove too heavy for transportation by air.

The United States has only very poor ores of uranium in moderate quantities. There is some good ore in Canada and former Czechoslovakia, while the most important source of uranium is in the Belgian Congo.

In view of this situation, you may think it desirable to have some permanent contact maintained between the Administration and the group of physicists working on chain reactions in America. One possible way of achieving this might be for you to entrust the task with a person who has your confidence and who could perhaps serve in an unofficial capacity. His task might comprise the following:

a) to approach Government Departments, keep them informed of the further development, and put forward recommendations for Government action, giving particular attention to the problem of securing a supply of uranium ore for the United States.

b) to speed up the experimental work, which is at present being carried on within the limits of the budgets of University laboratories, by providing funds, if such funds be required, through his contacts with private persons who are willing to make contributions for this cause, and perhaps also by obtaining co-operation of industrial laboratories which have necessary equipment.

I understand that Germany has actually stopped the sale of uranium from the Czechoslovakian mines which she has taken over. That she should have taken such early action might perhaps be understood on the ground that the son of the German Under-Secretary of State, von Weizsacker, is attached to the Kaiser-Wilhelm Institute in Berlin, where some of the American work on uranium is now being repeated.

Yours very truly,
Albert Einstein
(Einstein, 1939)

Later Einstein regretted signing this letter, but he need not have done so, because nothing actually happened because of it. Only a year later, in 1940, at the initiative of Winston Churchill, was the MAUD Committee created, which began work on the creation of the world's first atomic bomb. The results of MAUD's work were provided to the United States, and ultimately formed the basis of the Manhattan project, which ultimately developed the first atomic weapon in 1945. Right before the successful test of the American atomic bomb Einstein had written another letter to Roosevelt to dissuade him from using it, but this letter, too, was ineffectual.

The important point is that until then it was generally believed that nuclear physics was important for purely scientific research, and actual nuclear projects were too expensive, or simply "superfluous." That's why many countries, including the scientific leader in the field, France, did not attempt them, and only the US, USSR and Great Britain started committing large resources to the pursuit of the bomb.

But when the atomic bomb did become possible, it introduced a fundamentally new factor in international relations: because it was not just another weapon, and could not be offset by any number of other weapons, it changed the very structure of the balance of power in the world. Only with the advent of artificial intelligence is humankind again faced with the likelihood of a new revolution in global power balances.

Flyorov and Einstein

The Gilgamesh project or superhumans

"I will cut down the giant Humbaba, I will establish for myself a Name for eternity!"

The Epic of Gilgamesh

In the epic poem from ancient Mesopotamia, Gilgamesh, a fearless demigod, became famous for his continuous search for immortality. This idea has stirred people's imaginations since the beginning of times: everybody knows about the attempts of Chinese emperors and medieval alchemists to find the elixir of eternal life. None of them were successful. But now perhaps we are closer to solving this centuries-old riddle: the answer may lie in the application of nanotechnologies and artificial intelligence. Recent developments already provide ways to slow down the aging process and significantly increase life expectancy. In addition, medications for building memory resilience are being developed (Drexler, 1992).

In this context, the so-called superhumans will "possess unique abilities and unprecedented creative potential" which will put them above any political, social or economic system. This is how Yuval Noah Harari (2017) describes his vision of the new biological species of the future in his acclaimed book Homo Deus. This new species will emerge as the result of technological breakthroughs in the sphere of artificial intelligence, and in particular, with developments in nanorobotics and nano-assembly. The path to this revolutionary new stage in the evolution of the human mind is predicted to be long. Some say we will be there in about a century, while others do not expect this new era in human development to begin earlier than 200 years from now.

Today, the gene modification technology known as CRISPR-Cas9,[74] also called targeted editing of the genome or DNA, makes it possible to add, delete, or modify a gene in its exact location in the human genome. In 2018 this technology allowed an unauthorized Chinese scientist to edit human embryos in order to inactivate in them the CCR5 gene (Davies, 2019), which controls HIV, cholera and smallpox infections. Obviously, genome editing for human life extension is the goal, but regulations must first be changed.

In general, scientists have no doubts that tiny nanomachines will have a huge impact on our future due to the fundamental changes they will make, in medicine especially. As it is, the technology has progressed far beyond mere fantasies. For decades, science-fiction authors explored the subject of tiny robots inside human bodies, used for monitoring, purification and healing. But today the storyline in the 1966 movie "Fantastic Voyage," in which a submarine gets shrunk to microscopic size and injected into a patient's blood stream, is very close to reality.

In 1959, the brilliant physicist Richard Feynman was the first to comment about the possibility of developing nanomachines: "The principles of physics do not speak against the possibility of maneuvering things atom by atom" (Feynman, 1960). And in 1986, in his book Engines of Creation: The Coming Era of Nanotechnology (Drexler, 1986), the futurist Eric Drexler predicted the possibility of developing molecular assemblers, robots that will manipulate objects at the level of individual atoms and molecules.

In 1983, the French chemist Jean-Pierre Sauvage was the first to synthesize a compound of two mechanically bonded molecules. Later, in the years from 1991 to 1994, guided by Sauvage's ideas, the Scottish chemist J. Fraser Stoddart developed the very first molecular machines.[75] In 2004 he created a molecular elevator, and in 2007 a molecular muscle. He also developed a molecule-based computer chip with 20 kilobytes of memory.

In 2016, Stoddard shared the Nobel Prize in Chemistry with Ben Feringa and Jean-Pierre Sauvage for the design and synthesis of molecular machines.[76] The most important part of their work was to drive molecular systems out of equilibrium. Normally, all chemical systems tend to equilibrium—the lowest-energy state possible. Take our everyday life as an example. When we eat, the molecules in our bodies get energy from the food and "kick" our molecular systems out of equilibrium, to the higher energy level. Then biomolecules use the obtained energy to trigger the chemical reactions which are necessary to maintain our bodily functions.

The fundamental discoveries made by Sauvage, Stoddart and Feringa are already being applied in practice. Nanorobots have become part of our life, although not everyone understands what they are. These devices have dimensions in the range of 0.1 to 10 microns (a micron is one millionth of a meter), approximately the same size as a red blood cell. Bioengineered bots made from DNA are capable of delivering very small doses of drugs with great accuracy.

In 2017, researchers from the University of Alberta engineered a nanomachine for early diagnostics and the delivery of medications. The machines developed by those Canadian scientists are based on molecules or groups of molecules that can move (Peng, 2017).

2018 was marked by a new breakthrough in cancer treatment, when nanorobots were successfully used for the first time to treat cancer tumors in mice. This experiment was conducted by a group of scientists from the University of Arizona and the National Center for Nanoscience and Technology of the Chinese Academy of Sciences. The nanorobots they created are designed to act inside the blood vessels around cancer cells. In the experiment, the scientists injected nanorobots into the bodies of sick mice, and within hours after injection they reached the tumors. Then the nanorobots manipulated vascular cells in individual areas of the tumors, creating blood clots in the targeted tissue, which ultimately led to a slowing of the tumors' activity.

The authors of this study report that their concept can be used for treating many types of cancer, because the structure of the blood vessels feeding the tumors is mostly the same. Experiments with rodents have already demonstrated the effectiveness of nanorobots in treating breast, ovary, lung and skin cancers (Li, 2018). Currently scientists are studying the possibility of using nanobots for a number of other medical purposes, such as unblocking blood vessels in hard-to-reach spots, obtaining internal tissue samples and measuring the concentration of chemicals in internal organs.

Early in 2019 scientists in the University of Tokyo found a way to deliver specific drugs to tumors in parts of the body that are exceptionally difficult to access. The Y-shaped cation block (YBC) binds to certain therapeutic materials, forming a package just 18 nanometers wide. The package is small enough for it to overcome hard barriers on the way to tumor tissues in the treatment of brain or pancreas cancer (University of Tokyo, 2019).

Another promising area of research is gene therapy, which targets the genetic causes of diseases to reduce their effect. The idea is to inject a nucleic acid-based drug into the bloodstream, which then binds to a specific problem-causing gene and deactivates it. Typically, the drug is a small interfering RNA, but this RNA is very fragile and needs to be protected within a nanoparticle or it breaks down before reaching its target. According to Kanjiro Miyata, an associate professor at the University of Tokyo, the offending RNA can be easily eliminated from the body by enzymatic degradation or excretion. Scientists have already used polymers to fabricate a small and stable nanomachine for the delivery of RNA drugs to cancer tissues with a tight access barrier (Watanabe, 2019).

Nanotechnology is one of the most promising fields today (Anirudh, 2019). For centuries people dreamed of longevity and eternal youth. With developments in nanotechnology, these dreams are very likely to become reality one day.

It will also be possible to enhance human intelligence by connecting the brain to nano-engineering tools that use AI through what is called a "neurocomputer interface" (Gonfalonieri, 2018). Neuroprosthetic devices to restore vision, hearing and mobility are also the subject of intense research efforts. However, the ultimate goal of this technology is to increase the level of human intelligence, which is essential for the future era of singularity, or nearly essential.

Why is the neurocomputer interface so important? Elon Musk is convinced that we need that technology in order not to be forced out by artificial intelligence in the future (Valeriani, 2017). And his company Neuralink is already at work in pursuit of technological solutions to overcome this threat. In the summer of 2019, the company revealed a prototype of a device for the robotic injection into the brain of the thinnest filament electrodes, which are slightly thicker than a blood cell. These threads read signals from brain neurons that can be transformed into specific actions (Etherington, 2019).

The reading of brain signals is not a new technology, but in this case it is implemented on a completely different scale. Once, typing was made possible by the power of thought alone thanks to the connection of 256 electrodes. What could 10,000 electrodes be capable of?

Neuralink's minimum plan is to create a neuro-computer interface for paralyzed people, with the help of which they will be able to freely use computer equipment and smartphones. The prototype supports wireless communication of the device with a smartphone application. But the ultimate goal is to make human cognitive abilities equal with that of the artificial intelligence of the future. The company expects to receive permission to conduct clinical trials with human subjects participating in the next year.

What other possibilities does the neurocomputer interface present? The simplest thing is to manage bionic prostheses, which, receiving signals from the brain, will execute commands in the same way as normal parts of the body. Development in this direction opens up the very real possibility of creating an exoskeleton, a set of devices implanted in the human body that enhance physical capabilities.

To try to see the boundaries (which may be infinite) of the potential of the neurocomputer interface, we need to recall that absolutely everything that we consider to be reality is only the result of signal processing, using signals our brain receives from our sensory organs. This mean that, in theory, a close connection between a brain and a computer can simulate any "reality," instantly download text, audio and video information directly into the brain, and even communicate at the level of thought. However, if in the future we succeed in achieving a symbiosis with artificial intelligence and unite more than one mind into a single global neural network, then humanity might become the carrier of something that we could call divine consciousness.

According to some estimates (Panetta, 2018), the connection of the brain with artificial intelligence using a neurocomputer interface will be achieved within the next 10 years. Thus, a new era in the history of mankind may begin in the coming decade. That raises important ethical issues relating to the fundamental values of society. How can we prepare ourselves and our civilization for such radical changes? How can we face a future dominated by so many unknown variables?

The Asilomar principles

"Artificial intelligence could be the biggest event in
the history of our civilization. But it could also be
the last, unless we learn how to avoid the risks."

Stephen Hawking, 2016

In today's world, nothing is fraught with more opportunities and risks than artificial intelligence. As we discover new ways to apply it, the outlines of our future appear increasingly complex and unpredictable.

The development of AI in the health care system, as we found out, may lead us to a future in which potential diseases are predicted and cured even before they begin. However, using the same analysis, it will be possible to model negative scenarios related to the future. The ability to create medicines for any disease with the help of artificial intelligence will not eliminate the possibility someone could synthesize extremely powerful poisons. And technologies for treating genetic diseases with the help of nanorobots will make possible hidden intervention in the genomes of entire nations.

The trajectory of the development of virtual assistants looks no less contradictory. They have begun to accompany us everywhere and are coming to comprehend, better than ever, our beliefs, intentions, desires and emotions. All this brings targeting to a completely new level. And while this world is controlled by consumption, the development of virtual assistants may lock us into a narrowing spiral of our own temptations, with the high-tech corporations the beneficiaries.

The penetration of AI into the financial sector already makes it possible to receive a loan in mere seconds. But the conditions of that loan will depend on the assessed reliability of the borrower. In such a reality, the importance of a credit rating rises to a fundamentally new level, establishing rather strict social norms. Those who want more opportunities will learn to be as predictable as possible, and compliant with the behavioral algorithms that assess creditworthiness. Will this not cause an unprecedented increase in social inequality?

The benefits of implementing smart technologies in modern cities are indisputable. Safer transportation, less crime, a beautiful environment, and access to high-quality, personalized social services certainly increase our well-being. But with more opportunities, the price of failure also increases. The unified infrastructure management systems of smart cities will have to be maximally protected from cyberattacks and technical problems, since failure could lead to massive casualties, damage or at least an immediate surge in social anxiety.

Technology giants and supercorporations continue to accumulate influence globally because of their use of the most advanced solutions based on AI, and the continuing transition to a more digital reality, which allows the deep analysis of individual perceptions. The manipulation of public consciousness is not a new phenomenon; it has been practiced by leaders since time immemorial, but the possibilities offered by artificial intelligence make invisible forms of information warfare increasingly effective. And there are currently no international legal norms to limit such activities. As a result, we are witnessing a fragmentation of the digital space, as well as an increase in protectionism and international instability.

With the intensifying struggle for primacy in the field of artificial intelligence, our world, more than ever, needs new international laws for the digital age to provide the bedrock for a global community. Moreover, such laws must flexibly accommodate the rapidly changing realities of the digital age by being rooted in fundamental axioms, because it is impossible to predict the further development of AI. That is why many people, including Elon Musk and Stephen Hawking, have warned that the uncontrolled development of artificial intelligence poses a threat to the very future of humanity. Certainly, any autonomous AI systems, and not just weapons, should be subject to a strict regulatory framework developed and approved at the United Nations level.

Matthew Scherer, an expert on artificial intelligence, has noted that the growth of AI has so far occurred in a regulatory vacuum. With the exception of certain regulations relating to autonomous land and air vehicles, no laws and very few regulations have been written that specifically address the unique problems that society faces in its interaction with AI systems. And no court has developed standards for AI cases (Scherer, 2016). Traditional regulatory methods (product licensing, supervision of research and development, liability for offenses) seem inadequate to manage the dynamically evolving risks associated with intelligent and autonomous machines (Scherer, 2016). Such methods are characterized by rigidity, bureaucratic preoccupations, and very slow adoption processes in the face of rapidly developing technologies (Thierer, 2016).

In fact, the most appropriate and reasonable approach to the legal regulation of AI would be to formulate a new universal legal framework applicable to all such systems. One vital aspect, of course, is that complete security in the development and use of artificial intelligence systems will be a requirement.

What steps have already been taken in this direction? The report Artificial Intelligence and Life in 2030, prepared at Stanford University, made the following recommendations to pave the way for the legal regulations of AI ("Artificial Intelligence and Life," 2016; Ponkin, 2018, pp. 91-109):

– Determine a path to the accumulation of technical expertise in the field of AI at all levels of management;

– Eliminate perceived and actual obstacles to the study of the correct functioning, security, confidentiality and social impact of artificial intelligence systems;

– Increase public and private funding of interdisciplinary research to study the impact of AI on society.

A 2017 conference on the benefits and challenges of artificial intelligence, held in Pacific Grove, California, can be considered one of the most significant initiatives in this direction. Ray Kurzweil, Elon Musk, Stephen Hawking, Demis Hassabis, Yann LeCun and dozens of other internationally recognized scientists and experts in AI and related fields took part. They adopted the "Asilomar Principles of Artificial Intelligence," which lay the foundation for ethical research in this area:[77]

1.   The goal of AI research should be to create beneficial intelligence.

2.   Investments in AI should be accompanied by funding for research on ensuring its beneficial use, including thorny questions in computer science, economics, law, ethics, and social studies, such as:

– How can we make future AI systems highly robust, so that they do what we want without malfunctioning or getting hacked?

– How can we grow our prosperity through automation while maintaining people's resources and purpose?

– How can we update our legal systems to be more fair and efficient, to keep pace with AI, and to manage the risks associated with AI?

– What set of values should AI be aligned with, and what legal and ethical status should it have?

3.   There should be constructive and healthy exchange between AI researchers and policy-makers.

4.   A culture of cooperation, trust, and transparency should be fostered among researchers and developers of AI.

5.   Teams developing AI systems should actively cooperate to avoid corner-cutting on safety standards.

6.   AI systems should be safe and secure throughout their operational lifetime, and verifiably so where applicable and feasible.

7.   Failure Transparency. If an AI system causes harm, it should be possible to ascertain why.

8.   Any involvement by an autonomous system in judicial decision-making should provide a satisfac-

tory explanation auditable by a competent human authority.

9. Designers and builders of advanced AI systems are stakeholders in the moral implications of their use, misuse, and actions, with a responsibility and opportunity to shape those implications.

10. Highly autonomous AI systems should be designed so that their goals and behaviors can be assured to align with human values throughout their operation.

11. AI systems should be designed and operated so as to be compatible with ideals of human dignity, rights, freedoms, and cultural diversity.

12. People should have the right to access, manage and control the data they generate, given AI systems' power to analyze and utilize that data.

13. The application of AI to personal data must not unreasonably curtail people's real or perceived liberty.

14. AI technologies should benefit and empower as many people as possible.

15. The economic prosperity created by AI should be shared broadly, to benefit all of humanity.

16. Human Control: Humans should choose how and whether to delegate decisions to AI systems, to accomplish human-chosen objectives.

17. Non-subversion. The power conferred by control of highly advanced AI systems should respect and improve, rather than subvert, the social and civic processes on which the health of society depends.

18. AI Arms Race. An arms race in lethal autonomous weapons should be avoided.

19. Capability Caution. There being no consensus, we should avoid strong assumptions regarding upper limits on future AI capabilities.

20. Importance. Advanced AI could represent a profound change in the history of life on Earth, and should be planned for and managed with commensurate care and resources.

21. Risks posed by AI systems, especially catastrophic or existential risks, must be subject to planning and mitigation efforts commensurate with their expected impact.

22. AI systems designed to recursively self-improve or self-replicate in a manner that could lead to rapidly increasing quality or quantity must be subject to strict safety and control measures.

23. Superintelligence should only be developed in the service of widely shared ethical ideals, and for the benefit of all humanity rather than one state or organization.

The Asilomar Principles touch on very important guidelines for ensuring global security in the face of technological progress. First of all, the need for cooperation between AI researchers and politicians. Obviously, such interaction requires the creation of an international platform, the scale and authority of which should ensure the active involvement of all interested parties. This organization should engage in the formation of a new area of the global regulatory system that supports international security in the context of possible threats from the unfair use of AI capabilities.

In this regard, the international community should step up the fight against the problem of the so-called "black boxes," which inject ambiguity into the decision-making processes for artificial intelligence. This happens because the operation of machine learning algorithms is too complicated to be understood by humans.

Researchers will have to make extensive efforts to ensure the transparency of the algorithmic systems. Transparency should be made a non-negotiable requirement for any use of AI systems. Only in this way is it possible to develop universal legal norms that guarantee a fair and proportionate responsibility in case of violation.

The other most important issue is to ensure the confidentiality of personal data, for which there are still no comprehensive international standards, although in recent years there has been a noticeable movement in that direction. In the spring of 2016, for instance, the European Union adopted the General Data Protection Regulation (GDPR), unifying the rules for the protection of the personal data of all EU citizens. Of course, this set of rules does not provide uniform legal norms at the global level; but it is through such partial initiatives that international standards are born. For example, in the General Regulation there is a certain clause according to which free data migration between the EU and other countries is possible only if these countries have equivalent protection tools. Given that data sharing is now an essential part of international economic relations, other countries are likely to adopt the EU data protection laws, or equivalent laws of their own that meet the same general standards.

The need for a more equitable distribution of the benefits of AI is emerging as an extremely important pre-condition for global security. With the intensifying struggle of the superpowers and supercorporations for spheres of influence, with global threats such as climate change looming in the background, the question of reconciling and indeed unifying ethical and legal norms takes on unprecedented relevance. In that regard, the Asilomar Principles provide a most useful guideline that also speaks to the ethical issues.

Modern history offers examples of worldwide cooperation in the development of international ethical standards, as in the Universal Declaration of Human Rights and the promulgation of the Sustainable Development Goals. What they lack, aside from an enforcement mechanism, are provisions for the risks that arise in the process of developing artificial intelligence.

Futurologists engaged in AI research have warned us all about the emerging ethical issues. For example: "If the artificial intelligence of the future meets our expectations and turns out to be a thinking human-like robot with feelings and emotions, then we'll have to change the laws in order to embrace the role of robots in society. This means that it will be necessary to revise our existing legal system and adjust it in accordance with the changing needs of society" (Čerka, 2015).

Human-like robots (androids) of the future, as well as any objects with artificial intelligence, will need to have a certain legal status, taking into account their functions, technical characteristics and level of autonomy. Canadian scientist and futurologist George Dvorsky has suggested an entire set of rights for androids (Dvorsky, 2013):

- The right to not be shut down against its will
- The right to have full and unhindered access to its own source code
- The right to not have its own source code manipulated against its will
- The right to copy (or not copy) itself
- The right to privacy (namely the right to conceal its own internal mental states).

Other researchers have come up with the idea of an "ethical black box." For example, Alan Winfield, a professor of ethics for robots at the University of West Anglia in Bristol, is confident that robots and other autonomous systems must be equipped with an analogue of an airliner's production process recorder that continuously records sensor algorithms and the corresponding internal state data. The goal is to establish the cause of accidents in which the robot or AI machine could be at fault. Naturally, such control systems would facilitate measures to prevent similar accidents and errors in the future.

Science fiction authors have also made their contributions to the awareness of the ethical problems in the relationship between robots and humans, by offering rules of behavior for the intellectual systems of the future. Undoubtedly, the most famous such attempt, "Three Laws of Robotics," was presented by Isaac Asimov in his 1942 short story "Runaround".[78]

1. A robot may not injure a human being or, through inaction, allow a human being to come to harm.

2. A robot must obey the orders given it by human beings except where such orders would conflict with the First Law.

3. A robot must protect its own existence as long as such protection does not conflict with the First or Second Laws.

Later Asimov added to this set of laws a so-called zero law, to precede the others: "A robot may not harm humanity, or, by inaction, allow humanity to come to harm".

To summarize this chapter, it is worth noting the initiative of Elon Musk in creating the OpenAI company, whose declared aim is to develop AI for the benefit of humanity as a whole rather than single states or corporations. This initiative is attracting more and more supporters, especially among the developers of artificial intelligence. In July 2019, Microsoft announced an investment of $1 billion in this company. Today, when we are witnessing the dawn of an era of artificial intelligence, which offers the potential to solve the most serious problems of our time, the opportunities for global solutions are better than ever before.

Kazakhstan

"If we don't do it, then ten years from now we will be on the sidelines, swallowing the dust left by departing countries ...
This is precisely what the place and role of the country in the global community depends upon."

Nursultan Nazarbayev [79]

The acceleration of global trends in the development and implementation of artificial intelligence presages significant geopolitical changes in the coming years. Just as the industrial revolution once contributed to the growth of the United States and other advanced economies, AI technologies today can bring about radical changes in the global order.

Every day, the gap between the countries that have invested in artificial intelligence and those that have not is widening. And this is becoming a new cause of global inequality and anxiety.

Almost every industrialized country has announced major national initiatives for the development and implementation of artificial intelligence. The leaders, as we noted, are the United States and China. In order to keep up, other states have also begun to invest heavily in this area. For example, Singapore and the United Arab Emirates have spent significant resources to acquire "smart" technological capabilities, and are now among the most progressive countries in their regions.

The digital transformation of the leading sectors of national economies will open enormous additional opportunities for each country. In fact, our country is on the verge of forming a new state and public structure based on the technology of artificial intelligence. And Kazakhstan must become an integral part of the new technological environment, based on integrated global communications systems.

Kazakhstan has made significant progress in developing and implementing an e-government system (eGov). Today, 85.7% of public services are received by the population via electronic access. The eGov portal has 8.9 million registered users, and 90 public services can be obtained by using the mGov mobile app, which has 1.5 million users in Kazakhstan.[80]

In our country, the penetration level of home broadband networks is around 80% ("Postanovlenie," 2017). It is planned that the 5G standard will be up and running by the end of 2019 in the cities of Nur-Sultan, Almaty and Shymkent ("5G," 2019).

New technologies are being introduced into production processes in all major industries. Overall, by 2022, labor productivity in the mining industry should increase by 38.9%, and by 49.8% in the manufacturing industry, in which the share of large and medium-sized enterprises will be 11% ("Postanovlenie," 2017). Elements of "precision farming" are being actively introduced in the agriculture sector, in a number of pilot farms, with a 15-20% penetration percentage.[81]

Projects are also being implemented in Kazakhstan like the Astana Hub and the Astana International Financial Center, which were created to support the development and implementation of smart cities, big data, blockchain, AR, VR, IoT and more.

Building overall technical capacity in the field is the key requirement for the introduction of artificial intelligence in Kazakhstan. For this crucial task, Nazarbayev University plays a special role. Thanks to the timely decision made by the leader of the nation Nursultan Nazarbayev, that research university was founded in 2010 to function at American standards and produce advanced research. Today, its staff includes researchers from around the world specializing in data science, physics, quantum computing, bioengineering and robotics. Some 3,000 students have been trained by the university over the years, most of them specializing in science and technology. Today, with the support of the Government of Kazakhstan and the World Bank, a whole cluster for research and innovation in the field of artificial intelligence is being created at the University.

By 2018, Kazakhstan had already implemented a pilot project, Smart Aqkol, described in the beginning of this book. Here, integration of all levels of the smart-city infrastructure could be tested. And in July 2019, Kazakhstan's National Investment Corporation became one of the investors in the world's largest fund, Vision Fund 2, with a capitalization of $108 billion, joining the largest technology corporations and sovereign funds in the world.

For a country with a population of 18 million people, all these initiatives are extremely significant, and they form the necessary basis for piloting the various opportunities artificial intelligence offers.

After all, artificial intelligence is primarily a technology for people, and it's about building opportunities for other people.

For example, in Kazakhstan, the vast territory of the country, and the long distances between big cities and between villages within their regions, impede the achievement of economies of scale in spite of the overall expansion of the consumer market. Moreover, a significant portion of economic activity is generated by small enterprises and individual entrepreneurs who for the most part serve local or domestic needs, do not export their products, and sometimes do not even sell in neighboring regions.

Artificial intelligence solutions in business, finance, transport, the oil and gas industry, or a credit rating for business, as well as cloud platforms based on artificial intelligence that will connect entrepreneurs, developers, researchers and investors, could remove all of these barriers in an instant, and have a significant stimulating effect on the development of small and medium-sized businesses and help overcome the limitations caused by the territorial remoteness of the country's regions and the uneven concentration of consumers.

Integration into the overall system could give businesses new opportunities for product sales in other regions of Kazakhstan. As a result, the asymmetry of information will be reduced, which will also lead to a significant reduction of the shadow sector and a transition to electronic payments. The volume of the e-commerce market in Kazakhstan in 2018 reached $422.9 million, and the potential for further growth is enormous. All this will undoubtedly have a positive impact on economic growth in the country.

While views differ, the pilot project in the city of Akqol and examples of other smart cities prove how social and economic processes can be managed efficiently with AI, and how it will also have a beneficial impact on Kazakhstanis' overall well-being by reducing energy costs, optimizing consumption, minimizing the degree of environmental pollution and more.

Today citizens are constantly scanning numerous codes and digitizing their daily activities. In the near future, the use and deployment of wireless communications will provide high-speed internet and Bluetooth technology for content sharing and streaming.

The context is Kazakhstan's rapid urbanization: over the past five years, the urbanization level has increased from 56% to 62%, according to survey data. Three cities of the country—Shymkent, Almaty and Nur-Sultan—now have more than a million inhabitants each, and their populations are still increasing from year to year. In the cities of Karaganda, Aktobe and Pavlodar, there is also a rapid process of urbanization, up to 70% of the total population of those regions, while in other regions the level of urbanization is 60%. This growth presents challenges in the labor market, as well as housing shortages and congestion.

Building smart-city infrastructure in all of Kazakhstan's 17 big cities will undoubtedly lead to an increase in quality and efficiency in the operations of state organizations and local executive bodies, by generating massive amounts of information for artificial intelligence optimization processes to produce the best feasible solutions in real time. That will improve overall governance in everything from the regulation of traffic to crime prevention, and the more complete and efficient provision of public services, medical care and targeted social assistance.

In the realm of transportation, for example, citizens can determine their own preferences and create their own partnerships with enterprises. Tracking traffic every day, traffic control centers will be able to optimally allocate resources, including bus transportation, depending on the volume of traffic. This single "smart" component can benefit not only the citizenry at large, but also the national economy and government, by minimizing time lost in traffic jams, increasing productivity, reducing accident rates and ameliorating the environmental impact. With the introduction of artificial intelligence, private sector revenues may increase by 40% by 2035, reflecting equivalent productivity gains. Kazakhstan's transportation sector, one of the fastest growing areas of its economy, can generate huge benefits from larger investments in AI projects.

Smart cities also have smart health systems. Appointments with a doctor are made online, reducing secretarial work and friction caused by misunderstandings and errors. Doctors, for their part, will receive more rapid and complete access to patient profiles, and also to information about new medicines and medical technologies from the hospital's cloud system. The system also provides new ways for doctors to interact with patients via video link (remote reception).

Imagine: a patient from the remote Kyzylorda region receives high-quality medical consultation and treatment from the metropolitan medical center online. And the large number of profiles of patients in the cloud will help doctors quickly access cross-referenced disease data. In combination with the introduction of the technical solutions already mentioned, all this will give an impetus to medical progress in the country.

Of course, the realization of these ideas requires significant efforts, resources, and time. This is because we are faced with a strategic task: building a new economy based on innovative principles for the interconnection of people, objects and technologies.

Of course, this raises the question of protecting the rights and personal integrity of citizens. Some countries have started generating genomic data about every citizen with a view to using artificial intelligence to predict the possibility or actual presence of diseases in each individual, and to indicate the best methods of treatment. These actions are beginning to transform the health sector in many parts of the world. As it is, all technology companies that produce smartphones are collecting the biometric data of users, such as their fingerprints, voice, retinas and face shape. All this stimulates the development of biometric passports that will allow the abolition of paper documents for identity verification. On the other hand, whoever holds all this information can control people, knowing almost everything about each specific individual.

For that reason, as discussed above, we must create a universal legal framework applicable to all AI systems. This approach is supported by the rapid expansion of the possible ways artificial intelligence technologies can be used in various fields, from oil drilling to healthcare. But the legal, i.e., normative equalization of practices can lead us to underestimate the actual real-life risks, and the harm they can inflict on individuals and groups, or even on all citizens. That is why the legal standardization of AI activities and organizations should be carried out not on the scale of one country, but at the global level. And it is equally important to clearly understand that objects with artificial intelligence must have a certain legal status depending on their functions, technical characteristics and level of autonomy.

Kazakhstan needs to make significant efforts to formulate farsighted policies for data generation, data exchange and the use of data in multilateral cooperation. Those efforts should focus on the following two tasks: Kazakhstan must be able to use the technology of artificial intelligence to create and implement new technologies of artificial intelligence, and Kazakhstan must strengthen public confidence in the technologies of artificial intelligence, by protecting civil liberties and privacy.

In May 2019, the OECD member countries, as well as Argentina, Brazil, Colombia, Costa Rica, Peru and Romania, signed the OECD Principles for Artificial Intelligence, which state that governments, organizations and individuals must ensure that designers and operators are responsible for the proper and responsible functioning of AI systems.

Kazakhstan must adhere to those norms by supporting and implementing the Asilomar Principles. It is extremely important to maintain a delicate but durable balance between the interests of society and its individual members, between security guarantees and the need for experimentation and innovation.

The birth of AI itself raises many ethical questions, so our task must be to understand those questions and seek the best answers.

Epilogue

The world as we know it stands at a developmental crossroads. And the pivotal point of its transition to the next level is the advent of artificial intelligence.

The idea that "to know your future, you must know your past" has never been more valid. The discovery of the extraordinary capabilities of the uranium atom in the middle of the last century contributed to powerful breakthroughs not only in the development of the atomic bomb, but in nuclear power generation. The world witnessed the varied ways in which atomic energy emerged to be widely used in the span of a single generation.

Artificial intelligence is the new "uranium atom," and it is prone to duality, as well. It has the potential to solve problems that plague all humankind, but it can also lead to the development of super-weapons that could annihilate us as a species.

On the one hand, AI-led medical breakthroughs (nanorobots that cure cancer, molecular assemblers that create new molecules, exoskeletons for paraplegics, 3D printing of organs, genetic engineering, etc.) bring the promise of a bright future. On the other hand, they send a clear signal: we are moving closer and closer to the day when we may finally see the emergence of a superhuman, with an invulnerable immune system and unlimited intellectual capabilities.

Throughout history, many attempts have been made to develop mankind's "mystical" superpowers. However, the stages of our transformation followed an evolutionary path and spanned thousands of years. The laws of evolution constrained us, imposing limitations that forced our bodies to develop a certain way. But now we are approaching the era of artificial intelligence and facing the risks of an AI singularity: modern technology now allows us to "alter" ancient natural laws.

The problems associated with the coming AI era affect a variety of systems—molecular, organic, and those governing individuals in general, family units, and local communities. We can subsequently look at an even larger scale, at the level of cities, regions, countries, and continents. Finally, we—as humans living on Earth—realize the influence artificial intelligence can have on our entire planet. Note that this influence can be either positive and controlled or fatally destructive.

The duality of AI can be witnessed in everything. The emergence of the superhuman means that his primary characteristic will be domination over the average human. The subsequent development of supercorporations, supernations, and governments with AI technologies that are inaccessible to other countries gives birth to a new, drastically more unequal, world order. The world map already is divided into dominant countries, donor countries, leading countries and outsider countries. What is to stop the emergence of rogue AI nations and AI terrorism?

It's imperative that now, on the brink of the AI singularity, governments come together and develop uniform and lasting laws to govern the global use of artificial intelligence. New technologies should contribute to human progress and global peace. This is a central issue for many countries across the world, including Kazakhstan.

Can we build an effective system that ushers in the AI future of Kazakhstan and integrates our country into the global community of leaders of the new technological revolution? Will we be able to maintain this position as we stand on the threshold of AI triumph, and join the other developed countries that have a full-fledged voice in all discussions and decision-making revolving around the global tasks and challenges of the artificial intelligence era?

Kazakhstan needs answers to these critical questions now. Our AI future begins today.

Contest entries for "Kazakhstan of my dreams"

In the summer of 2019, there was an art contest called "Kazakhstan of my dreams," in which Kazakhstani artists presented their vision of the future of Kazakhstan. Many of these artworks envisioned the coming together of man and smart technology.

Artworks of the contest "Kazakhstan of my dreams"

Veronica Valeryevna Morskaya, "The distant and beautiful future"

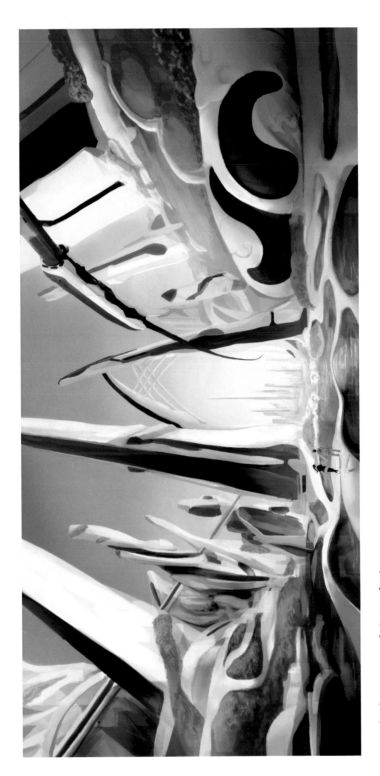

Vladimir Sergeevich Savitsky,
"Kazakhstan 2120"

Artworks of the contest "Kazakhstan of my dreams"

Sophia Son,
"The Land of My Dreams"

Akmaral Shaimagam-betova, "Kyz Kuu" (named for a traditional game)

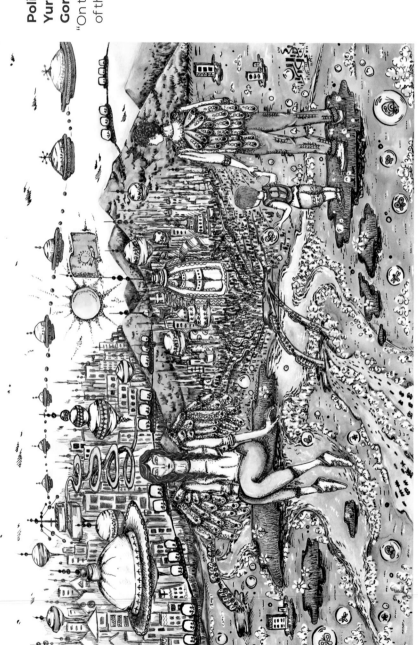

Polina Yurievna Goryaeva, "On the Wings of the Future"

Talgat Boranbaevich Serikov,
"QAZAQSTAN 2119 Heritage City"

Artworks of the contest "Kazakhstan of my dreams"

Stanislav Anastasyev, "The distant and beautiful future"

Bibliography

"5G poiavitsia v trekh gorodakh Kazakhstana do kontsa goda." Tengrinews.kz (May 21, 2019). Available at: https://tengrinews.kz/kazakhstan_news/5G-poyavitsya-v-treh-gorodah-kazahstana-do-kontsa-goda-369539/ (accessed May 25, 2019)

"10 bogateishikh liudei mira. Reiting Forbes." 2019. Forbes Russia (March 5). Available at: https://www.forbes.ru/milliardery-photogallery/372967-10-bogateyshih-lyudey-mira-reyting-forbes?photo=8 (accessed May 12, 2019).

Accenture. 2017. "Artificial Intelligence: Healthcare's New Nervous System." Available at: https://www.accenture.com/_acnmedia/PDF-49/Accenture-Health-Artificial-Intelligence.pdf#zoom=50 (accessed April 5, 2019).

Agence France Presse. 2018. "Computer learns to detect skin cancer more accurately than doctors." The Guardian (May 29). Available at: https://www.theguardian.com/society/2018/may/29/skin-cancer-computer-learns-to-detect-skin-cancer-more-accurately-than-a-doctor (accessed April 12, 2019).

Ali, Umar. 2019a. "BP invests in artificial intelligence for upstream business." Offshore Technology (January 28). Available at: https://www.offshore-technology.com/digital-disruption/ai/bp-artificial-intelligence-investment/ (accessed July 18, 2019).

Ali, Umar. 2019b. "OGA launches UK's first oil and gas national data repository." Offshore Technology (March 25). Available at: https://www.offshore-technology.com/news/oga-national-data-repository/ (accessed July 20, 2019).

Andriotis, Anna M. 2019. "Shopping at Discount Stores Could Help Get You a Loan." The Wall Street Journal (March 4). Available at: http://webreprints.djreprints.com/4542120583621.html (accessed July 15, 2019).

Anirudh, VK. 2019. "Can Nanotechnology Build The AI Of The Future?" Analytics India Magazine (January 30). Available at: https://www.analyticsindiamag.com/can-nanotechnology-build-the-ai-of-the-future/ (accessed April 3, 2019).

Aouf, Rima S. 2019a. "Continental's autonomous robot dogs could help deliver parcels." Dezeen (January 10). Available at: https://www.dezeen.com/2019/01/10/continental-autonomous-robot-dogs-parcel-delivery/ (accessed July 14, 2019).

Aouf, Rima S. 2019b. "Boeing's self-piloted passenger drone completes first test flight." Dezeen (January 28). Available at: https://www.dezeen.com/2019/01/28/boeing-autonomous-passenger-drone-flying-car/ (accessed July 19, 2019).

Arnold, Martin. 2018. "HSBC brings in AI to help spot money laundering." Financial Times (April 9). Available at: https://www.ft.com/content/b9d7daa6-3983-11e8-8b98-2f31af407cc8 (accessed July 7, 2019).

"Arterys Receives First FDA Clearance for Broad Oncology Imaging Suite with Deep Learning." 2018. Cision PR Newswire (February 15, 2018). Available at: https://www.prnewswire.com/news-releases/arterys-receives-first-fda-clearance-for-broad-oncology-imaging-suite-with-deep-learning-300599275.html (accessed April 9, 2019).

"Artificial Intelligence and Life in 2030: One Hundred Year Study on Artificial Intelligence." 2016. Report of the 2015 Study Panel, Stanford, CA, Available at: https://ai100.stanford.edu/sites/g/files/sbiybj9861/f/ai_100_report_0831fnl.pdf (accessed April 11, 2019).

"Autonomous Vehicle Market by Autonomy Level (Semi-autonomous [Level 1 to 4] and Fully Autonomous [Level 5], Vehicle Powertrain, Components, and Supporting Tech (5G, AI, Edge Computing, Smart Buildings, and more), Globally and Regionally 2019—2024." 2019. Research and Markets (January). Available at: https://www.researchandmarkets.com/research/mc83t6/autonomous?w=12 (accessed July 18, 2019).

Baker, Liana B. 2017. "SoftBank invests in industrial software firm OSIsoft." Reuters (June 1). Available at:

https://www.reuters.com/article/us-softbank-funding-osisoft/softbank-invests-in-industrial-software-firm-osisoft-idUSKBN18S3G9 (accessed June 17, 2019).

Ballinger, Brandon et al. 2018. "DeepHeart: Semi-Supervised Sequence Learning for Cardiovascular Risk Prediction." Association for the Advancement of Artificial Intelligence. Available at: https://www.aaai.org/ocs/index.php/AAAI/AAAI18/paper/view/16967/15916 (accessed April 13, 2019).

Barlow, John P. 1996. "A Declaration of the Independence of Cyberspace." Available at: http://editions-hache.com/essais/pdf/barlow1.pdf (accessed May 21, 2019).

Basulto, Dominic. 2012. "Why Ray Kurzweil's Predictions Are Right 86% of the Time." Big Think (December 13). Available at: https://bigthink.com/endless-innovation/why-ray-kurzweils-predictions-are-right-86-of-the-time (accessed May 21, 2019).

Bendett, Samuel. 2018. "Here's How the Russian Military Is Organizing to Develop AI." Defense One (July 20). Available at: https://www.defenseone.com/ideas/2018/07/russian-militarys-ai-development-roadmap/149900/ (accessed July 26, 2019).

Bendett, Samuel. 2019. "Putin Orders Up a National AI Strategy." Defense One (January 31). Available at: https://www.defenseone.com/technology/2019/01/

putin-orders-national-ai-strategy/154555/ (accessed July 14, 2019).

Blomberg, Stig N. et al. 2019. "Machine learning as a supportive tool to recognize cardiac arrest in emergency calls." Official Journal of the European Resuscitation Council 138, (May): 322-329.

Borowiec, Steven. 2016. "AlphaGo seals 4-1 victory over Go grandmaster Lee Sedol." The Guardian (March 15). Available at: https://www.theguardian.com/technology/2016/mar/15/googles-alphago-seals-4-1-victory-over-grandmaster-lee-sedol (accessed April 2, 2019).

Burgess, Matt. 2018. "Is AI the new electricity?" The Guardian (November 12). Available at: https://www.theguardian.com/future-focused-it/2018/nov/12/is-ai-the-new-electricity (accessed April 14, 2019).

Burnett, Richard. 2017. "The most helpful 'banking assistant' on Facebook." Wells Fargo Stories (July 26). Available at: https://www.stories.wf.com/helpful-banking-assistanton-Facebook/ (accessed July 18, 2019).

Byrnes, Nanette. 2017. "As Goldman Embraces Automation, Even the Masters of the Universe Are Threatened." MIT Technology Review (February 7). Available at: https://www.technologyreview.com/s/603431/as-goldman-embraces-automation-even-the-masters-of-the-universe-are-threatened/ (accessed July 14, 2019).

Cadwalladr, Carole and Emma Graham-Harrison. 2018. "Revealed: 50 million Facebook profiles harvested for Cambridge Analytica in major data breach." The Guardian (March 17). Available at: https://www. theguardian.com/news/2018/mar/17/cambridge-analytica-Facebook-influence-us-election (accessed April 30, 2019).

Calderone, Len. 2018. "Autonomous Trucks Will be Rolling on the Highway." Robotics Tomorrow (February 15). Available at: https://www.roboticstomorrow. com/article/2018/02/autonomous-trucks-will-be-rolling-on-the-highway/11379/ (accessed July 6, 2019).

Campbell, Murray, A. Joseph Hoane, and Feng-hsiung Hsu. 2002. "Deep Blue." Artificial Intelligence 134, no. 1-2 (January): 57-83.

Čerka, Paulius, Jurgita Grigienė and Gintarė Sirbikytė. 2015. "Liability for damages caused by artificial intelligence." Computer Law & Security Review 31, no. 3 (June): 376-389.

China AI Development Report. 2018. Prepared by China Institute for Science and Technology Policy at Tsinghua University. Available at: http://www.sppm. tsinghua.edu.cn/eWebEditor/UploadFile/China_AI_development_report_2018.pdf (accessed May 25, 2019).

Chui, Michael and Sankalp Malhotra, 2018. "AI adoption advances, but foundational barriers remain." McKinsey Global Institute. Available at: https://www.mckinsey.com/featured-insights/artificial-intelligence/ai-adoption-advances-but-foundational-barriers-remain (accessed July 3, 2019).

Cision PRWeb. 2017. "Experian Partners With Lenddo to use its Solution in Financial Inclusion efforts." Cision PRWeb (February 15). Available at: http://www.prweb.com/releases/lenddo/partners-with-experian/prweb14072502.htm (accessed July 5, 2019).

"A Collaboration in Curiosity: ExxonMobil and MIT Explore the Oceans." 2016. EnergyFactor (December 2016). Available at: https://energyfactor.exxonmobil.com/news/mit-collaboration/ (accessed June 26, 2019).

Comstock, Jonah. 2018. "SkinVision gets $7.6M to continue expanding skin cancer app." Mobihealthnews (July 30). Available at: https://www.mobihealthnews.com/content/skinvision-gets-76m-continue-expanding-skin-cancer-app (accessed April 12, 2019).

Condon, Stephanie. 2018. "Bank of America debuts its AI-powered assistant, Erica." ZDNet (May 18). Available at: https://www.zdnet.com/article/bank-of-america-debuts-its-ai-powered-assistant-erica/ (accessed July 21, 2019).

Cronk, Terri M. 2019. "DOD Unveils Its Artificial Intelligence Strategy." US Department of Defense (February 12). Available at: https://dod.defense.gov/News/Article/Article/1755942/dod-unveils-its-artificial-intelligence-strategy/ (accessed June 24, 2019).

Davies, Kevin. 2019. "CRISPR's China Crisis." Genetic Engineering & Biotechnology News (January 11). Available at: https://www.genengnews.com/insights/crisprs-china-crisis/ (accessed April 10, 2019).

Dent, Steve. 2017. "For a dollar, an AI will examine your medical scan." Engadget (October 27). Available at: https://www.engadget.com/2017/10/27/for-a-dollar-an-ai-will-examine-your-medical-scan/ (accessed April 17, 2019).

Diamandis, Peter H. 2015. "Ray Kurzweil's Mind-Boggling Predictions for the Next 25 Years." Singularity Hub (January 26). Available at: https://singularityhub.com/2015/01/26/ray-kurzweils-mind-boggling-predictions-for-the-next-25-years/#sm.00001ue2ff8frifegq0g29fowsq6x, (accessed April 14, 2019).

Drexler, Eric. 1986. *Engines of Creation: The Coming Era of Nanotechnology*. New York: Anchor Books, Doubleday.

Drexler, Eric. 1992. *Nanosystems*. New York: John Wiley & Sons.

Dvorsky, George. 2013. "Would it be evil to build a functional brain inside a computer?" Gizmodo (June 27). Available at: https://io9.gizmodo.com/would-it-be-evil-to-build-a-functional-brain-inside-a-c-598064996 (accessed April 23, 2019).

Einstein, Albert. 1939. Letter to President Roosevelt. Available at: https://www.osti.gov/opennet/manhattan-project-history/Resources/einstein_letter_photograph.htm#1 (accessed August 20, 2019).

Elias, Manuel. 2017. "At UN, robot Sophia joins meeting on artificial intelligence and sustainable development." UN News (October 11). Available at: https://news.un.org/en/story/2017/10/568292-un-robot-sophia-joins-meeting-artificial-intelligence-and-sustainable (accessed April 26, 2019).

Engelmann, Severin et al. 2018. "Clear Sanctions, Vague Rewards: How China's Social Credit System Currently Defines 'Good' and 'Bad' Behavior." In Proceedings of the Conference on Fairness, Accountability, and Transparency. ACM, 69-78.

Etherington, Darrell. 2019. "Elon Musk's Neuralink looks to begin outfitting human brains with faster input and output starting next year." TechCrunch (July 16). Available at: https: //techcrunch.com/2019/07/16/elon-musks-neuralink-looks-to-begin-outfitting-human-brains-with-faster-input-and-output-starting-next-year/ (accessed July 24, 2019).

Faggella, Daniel. 2019. "Machine Learning in Healthcare: Expert Consensus from 50+ Executives." Emerj Artificial Intelligence Research (January 31). Available at: https://emerj.com/ai-market-research/machine-learning-in-healthcare-executive-consensus/ (accessed April 8, 2019).

Fairs, Marcus. 2018. "London rooftops snapped up for 'vertiports' as drone travel moves closer." Dezeen (August 23). Available at: https://www.dezeen.com/2018/08/23/skyports-barr-gazetas-london-rooftops-vertiports-drones-technology/ (accessed July 17, 2019).

Feynman, Richard P. 1960. "There's Plenty of Room at the Bottom." Caltech Engineering and Science, vol 23:5 (February): 22-36.

FICO. 2016. "FICO and Lenddo Partner to Extend Credit Reach in India." FICO.COM (October 3). Available at: https://www.fico.com/en/newsroom/fico-and-lenddo-partner-to-extend-credit-reach-in-india-10-03-2016 (accessed June 24, 2019).

Ford Media Center. 2017. "Ford Credit and Zestfinance team up to enhance risk modeling, better serve consumers and lower credit losses." FordMediaCenter (August 25). Available at: https://media.ford.com/content/fordmedia/fna/us/en/news/2017/08/25/ford-credit-and-zest-finance-team-up.html (accessed July 14, 2019).

Gaur, Shantanu. 2017. "3 hurdles to bringing medical devices to the U.S. market." STAT (September 27). Available at: https://www.statnews.com/2017/09/27/medical-device-approval-fda/ (accessed April 8, 2019).

Gibson, Eleanor. 2017. "Uber and NASA to launch flying taxi service by 2020." Dezeen (November 9). Available at: https://www.dezeen.com/2017/11/09/uber-partners-with-nasa-to-launch-flying-taxi-service-by-2020-transport-design/ (accessed July 14, 2019).

The Great Hack. 2019. Directed by Karim Amer and Jehane Noujaim. A Netflix production. Available by subscription: https://www.netflix.com/title/80117542?s=i (accessed July 25, 2019).

Giridharadas, Anand. 2019. *Winners Take All: The Elite Charade of Changing the World.* Penguin Books, Limited, 2019.

Gonfalonieri, Alexandre. 2018. "A Beginner's Guide to Brain-Computer Interface and Convolutional Neural Networks." Towards Data Science (November 26). Available at: https://towardsdatascience.com/a-beginners-guide-to-brain-computer-interface-and-convolutional-neural-networks-9f35bd4af948 (accessed April 30, 2019).

Haenssle, Holger A. et al. 2018. "Man against machine: diagnostic performance of a deep learning convolutional neural network for dermoscopic melanoma recognition in comparison to 58 dermatologists." Annals of Oncology 29, no. 8 (May):1836-1842.

Hall, Peter. 2000. "Creative Cities and Economic Development." Urban Studies 37, no. 4 (April): 639-649.

Harari Yuval N. 2017. *Homo Deus: A Brief History of Tomorrow.* Harper; 1st Edition.

"The history of artificial intelligence. From Turing to Watson: The development of thinking systems." 2018. Available at: https://www.bosch.com/stories/history-of-artificial-intelligence/ (accessed April 9, 2019).

Hitti, Natashah. 2018a. "Airbus' self-piloted air taxi takes to the skies." Dezeen (February 2). Available at: https://www.dezeen.com/2018/02/02/airbus-self-piloted-vahana-air-taxi-takes-completes-first-test-flight/ (accessed July 10, 2019).

Hitti, Natashah. 2018b. "'World's first' commercial flying car unveiled at Geneva Motor Show." Dezeen (March 13). Available at: https://www.dezeen.com/2018/03/13/worlds-first-commercial-flying-car-unveiled-at-geneva-motor-show/?li_source=LI&li_medium=bottom_block_1 (accessed July 24, 2019).

Hitti, Natashah. 2019a. "Muji's driverless Gacha bus takes to the roads in Helsinki." Dezeen (March 15). Available at: https://www.dezeen.com/2019/03/15/gacha-self-driving-bus-muji-sensible-4/?li_

source=LI&li_medium=bottom_block_1 (accessed July 9, 2019).

Hitti, Natashah. 2019b. "FedEx's autonomous robot SameDay Bot delivers packages to your doorstep." Dezeen (February 28). Available at: https://www.dezeen.com/2019/02/28/sameday-bot-fedex-delivery-robot/ (accessed July 13, 2019).

Hitti, Natashah. 2019c. "Amazon to deliver purchases by drone 'within months.'" Dezeen (June 6). Available at: https://www.dezeen.com/2019/06/06/amazon-prime-air-drone-news/ (accessed June 24, 2019).

Horsley, Jamie. 2018. "China's Orwellian Social Credit Score Isn't Real." Foreign Policy (November 16). Available at: https://foreignpolicy.com/2018/11/16/chinas-orwellian-social-credit-score-isnt-real/ (accessed April 27, 2019).

Husseini, Talal. 2018. "Shell partners with Microsoft to accelerate offshore innovation." Offshore Technology. (September 21). Available at: https://www.offshore-technology.com/news/shell-microsoft-offshore-innovation/ (accessed July 15, 2019).

"Iandeks nachnet razrabotku bespilotnykh avto v Izraile." 2019. Kommersant" (June 11). Available at: https://www.kommersant.ru/doc/3998742 (accessed July 6, 2019).

"Iandeks ne iskliuchil poiavlenie bespilotnykh taksi v Moskve k 2022." 2019. Forbes (January 25). Available at: https://forbes.kz/news/2019/01/25/newsid_191530 (accessed May 4, 2019).

"Iandeks uvelichit park testovykh bespilotnikov do 100 mashin." 2019. Kommersant" (May 24). Available at: https://www.kommersant.ru/doc/3981514 (accessed July 6, 2019).

IMF (International Monetary Fund). 2019. *World Economic Outlook.* IMF World Economic and Financial Surveys. Washington. Available at: https://www.imf.org/external/pubs/ft/weo/2018/02/weodata/index.aspx (accessed April 25, 2019).

"Japan gain reported in computers." 1984. *The New York Times,* Nov. 12, 1984. Available at: https://www.nytimes.com/1984/11/12/business/japan-gain-reported-in-computers.html (accessed April 21, 2019).

Johnson, Khari. 2018. "Baidu Research's breast cancer detection algorithm outperforms human pathologists." VentureBeat (June 18). Available at: https://venturebeat.com/2018/06/18/baidu-researchs-breast-cancer-detection-algorithm-outperforms-human-pathologists/ (accessed April 12, 2019).

JPMorgan Chase & Co. 2017. *Annual Report 2016.* New York. Available at: https://www.jpmorganchase.com/corporate/investor-relations/document/2016-annualreport.pdf (accessed July 12, 2019).

Kabza, Milena. 2019. "Artificial intelligence is taking over financial services." Central European Financial Observer (February 7). Available at: https://financialobserver.eu/poland/artificial-intelligence-is-taking-over-financial-services/ (accessed July 18, 2019).

Kelley, Steven. 2019. "Seeing AI: Artificial Intelligence for blind and visually impaired users." VisionAware. Available at: https://www.visionaware.org/info/everyday-living/helpful-products/using-apps/seeing-ai-app/1235 (accessed April 28, 2019).

Kharpal, Arjun. 2017. "China wants to be a $150 billion world leader in AI in less than 15 years." CNBC (July 21). Available at: https://www.cnbc.com/2017/07/21/china-ai-world-leader-by-2030.html (accessed July 15, 2019).

Khokhlova, Dar'ia. 2017. "Kak 'Iandeks' sozdaval 'Alisu'." VC.RU (October 10). Available at: https://vc.ru/future/26878-ya-alice (accessed July 8, 2019).

Kiniakina, Ekaterina, Aleksei Sivashenkov and Aleksandr Baulin. 2019. "Yandeks i hyundai do kontsa goda predstaviat sovmestnye bespilotniki." Forbesworld (February 19). Available at: https://www.forbes.ru/tehnologii/373485-yandeks-i-hyundai-do-konca-goda-predstavyat-sovmestnye-bespilotniki (accessed July 11, 2019).

Kirkpatrick, David. 2011. *The Facebook Effect: The Inside Story of the Company That Is Connecting the World.* New York: Simon & Schuster.

Knapp, Alex. 2018. "Microsoft Partners With Fintech Startup ZestFinance To Bring Transparency To AI-Powered Financial Models." Forbes (December19). Available at: https://www.forbes.com/sites/alexknapp/2018/12/19/microsoft-partners-with-fintech-startup-zestfinance-to-bring-transparency-to-ai-powered-financial-models/#70bbad591c18 (accessed July 11, 2019).

KOFAX. 2019. *The JPMorgan Chase Buyer's Guide to Robotic, Process Automation.* Available at: https://www.kofax.com/learn/ebooks/-/media/Files/E-books/EN/eb_abm-jpmorganchase-kofax-rpa-buyers-guide_en.pdf (accessed July 4, 2019).

KPMG. 2018. Autonomous Vehicles Readiness Index: Assessing countries' openness and preparedness for autonomous vehicles. KPMG International. Available at: https://assets.kpmg/content/dam/kpmg/tw/pdf/2018/03/KPMG-Autonomous-Vehicle-Readiness-Index.pdf (accessed April 19, 2019).

Kubota, Taylor. 2017. "Deep learning algorithm does as well as dermatologists in identifying skin cancer." Stanford News (January 25). Available at: https://news.stanford.edu/2017/01/25/artificial-intelligence-used-identify-skin-cancer/ (accessed April 24, 2019).

Kumar, Rahul and Richa. 2018. Autonomous Vehicle Market Outlook—2026. Allied Market Research. Available at: https://www.alliedmarketresearch.com/autonomous-vehicle-market (accessed April 24, 2019).

Kurzweil, Raymond. 2005a. *The Singularity is Near: When Humans Transcend Biology.* New York: Penguin.

Kurzweil, Raymond. 2005b. "Human life: The next generation." New Scientist (September 24). Available at: http://www.singularity.com/NewScienceArticle.pdf (accessed April 15, 2019).

Lago, Cristina and Charlotte Trueman. 2019. "How Singapore is using artificial intelligence." CIO (March 12). Available at: https://www.cio.com/article/3292616/how-singapore-is-using-artificial-intelligence.html (accessed July 13, 2019).

Lebada, Ana M. 2017. "Second Committee Considers Role of AI in Advancing SDGs." SDG Knowledge Hub (October 12). Available at: https://sdg.iisd.org/news/second-committee-considers-role-of-ai-in-advancing-sdgs/ (accessed April 14, 2019).

Lee, Jamie. 2017. "OCBC chatbot 'Emma' helps customers sign $70m in home loans." The Straits Times (November 7). Available at: https://www.straitstimes.com/business/banking/ocbc-chatbot-emma-helps-customers-sign-70m-in-home-loans (accessed July 6, 2019).

Lee, Kai-Fu. 2018. *AI Superpowers: China, Silicon Valley and the New World Order.* Boston: Houghton Mifflin Harcourt.

Lee, Sang K. et al. 2016. *International Case Studies of Smart Cities: Songdo, Republic of Korea.* Inter-American Development Bank. Available at: https://publications.iadb.org/en/international-case-studies-smart-cities-songdo-republic-korea (accessed April 27, 2019).

Lemola, Johanna. 2018. "Self-driving Bus on Helsinki RobobusLine Goes to Scheduled Service." GlobeNewswire (May 14). Available at: https://www.globenewswire.com/news-release/2018/05/14/1501889/0/en/Self-driving-Bus-on-Helsinki-RobobusLine-Goes-to-Scheduled-Service.html (accessed July 10, 2019).

Leviathan, Yaniv and Yossi Matias. 2018. "Google Duplex: An AI System for Accomplishing Real-World Tasks over the Phone." Google AI Blog (May 8). Available at: https://ai.googleblog.com/2018/05/duplex-ai-system-for-natural-conversation.html (accessed April 11, 2019).

Li, Suping et al. 2018. "A DNA nanorobot functions as a cancer therapeutic in response to a molecular trigger in vivo." Nature Biotechnology 36, (February): 258-264. Available at: https://www.nature.com/articles/nbt.4071 (accessed April 30, 2019).

Mallonee, Laura. 2018. "Photographing a Robot isn't Just Point and Shoot." WIRED Magazine (March 29).

Available at: https://www.wired.com/story/photo-graphing-a-robot/ (accessed April 15, 2019).

Mammoser, Gigen. 2018. "AI May Be Better at Detecting Skin Cancer Than Your Derm." Healthline Media. Available at: https://www.healthline.com/health-news/ai-may-be-better-at-detecting-skin-cancer-than-your-derm#1 (accessed April 24, 2019)

Marr, Bernard. 2018a. "The Key Definitions of Artificial Intelligence (AI) That Explain Its Importance." Forbes (February 14). Available at: https://www.forbes.com/sites/bernardmarr/2018/02/14/the-key-definitions-of-artificial-intelligence-ai-that-explain-its-importance/#3c4c65554f5d (accessed April 13, 2019).

Marr, Bernard. 2018b. "The Amazing Ways Chinese Tech Giant Alibaba Uses Artificial Intelligence And Machine Learning." Forbes (July 23). Available at: https://www.forbes.com/sites/bernardmarr/2018/07/23/the-amazing-ways-chinese-tech-giant-alibaba-uses-artificial-intelligence-and-machine-learning/#ab38968117a9 (accessed July 29, 2019).

Marr, Bernard. 2019. "Chinese Social Credit Score: Utopian Big Data Bliss or Black Mirror on Steroids?" Forbes (January 21). Available at: https://www.forbes.com/sites/bernardmarr/2019/01/21/chinese-social-credit-score-utopian-big-data-bliss-or-black-mirror-on-steroids/#799a011648b8 (accessed April 8, 2019).

"Masdar City launches autonomous shuttle." 2018. Gulf News (October 22). Available at: https://gulfnews. com/uae/transport/masdar-city-launches-autonomous-shuttle-1.2292558 (accessed April 26, 2019).

"Masdar City unveils sustainable smart home farming." 2019. Gulf News (January 17). Available at: https://gulfnews.com/uae/environment/masdar-city-unveils-sustainable-smart-home-farming-1.61498952 (accessed April 30, 2019).

Mastercard. 2015. "Mastercard Identity Check: Facial Recognition Biometrics." (October 6). Available at: https://newsroom.mastercard.com/videos/mastercard-identity-check-facial-recognition-biometrics/ (accessed July 5, 2019).

McBride, Stephen. 2019. "Two big updates on the 5G rollout in America." RiskHedge (May 30). Available at: https://www.riskhedge.com/post/two-big-updates-on-the-5g-rollout-in-america (accessed July 19, 2019).

McKinsey & Company. 2018a. *Notes from the AI Frontier: Applying AI for Social Good.* Discussion Paper. December 2018. McKinsey Global Institute. Available at: https://www.mckinsey.com/~/media/McKinsey/Featured%20Insights/Artificial%20Intelligence/Applying%20artificial%20intelligence%20for%20social%20good/MGI-Applying-AI-for-social-good-Discussion-paper-Dec-2018.ashx (accessed April 22, 2019).

McKinsey & Company. 2018b. *Notes from the AI Frontier: Modeling the Impact of AI on the World Economy.* Discussion Paper. September 2018. McKinsey Global Institute. Available at: https://www.mckinsey.com/~/ media/McKinsey/Featured%20Insights/Artificial%20 Intelligence/Notes%20from%20the%20frontier%20 Modeling%20the%20impact%20of%20AI%20on%20 the%20world%20economy/MGI-Notes-from-the-AI-frontier-Modeling-the-impact-of-AI-on-the-world-economy-September-2018.ashx (accessed April 21, 2019).

Mekhanik, Aleksandr. "'Ochen' zhelatel'no Vashe prisutstvie.'" Published on Stimul. Available at: https://stimul.online/historical-dates/ochen-zhelatel-no-vashe-prisutstvie/ (accessed August 20, 2019).

"Memorandum on the Establishment of the Joint Artificial Intelligence Center." 2018. United States Department of Defense (June 27). Available at: https:// admin.govexec.com/media/establishment_of_the_ joint_artificial_intelligence_center_osd008412-18_r.... pdf (accessed April 14, 2019).

Metz, Cade. 2018. "Artificial Intelligence Is Now a Pentagon Priority. Will Silicon Valley Help?" *The New York Times* (August 26). Available at: https://www. nytimes.com/2018/08/26/technology/pentagon-arti-ficial-intelligence.html (accessed April 14, 2019).

"Microsoft's Xiaoice, China's newest fashion designer, unveils her first collection for 2019." 2018. NEWS.MICROSOFT.COM (November 12). Available at: https://news.microsoft.com/apac/2018/11/12/microsofts-xiaoice-chinas-newest-fashion-designer-unveils-her-first-collection-for-2019/ (accessed April 14, 2019).

Minter, Adam. 2019. "Why Big Brother Doesn't Bother Most Chinese." Bloomberg Opinion (January 25). Available at: https://www.bloomberg.com/opinion/articles/2019-01-24/why-china-s-social-credit-systems-are-surprisingly-popular (accessed April 6, 2019).

Molteni, Megan. 2017. "If You Look at X-Rays or Moles For a Living, AI Is Coming For Your Job." WIRED Magazine (January 25). Available at: https://www.wired.com/2017/01/look-x-rays-moles-living-ai-coming-job/ (accessed April 8, 2019).

Moor, James. 2006. "The Dartmouth College Artificial Intelligence Conference: The Next Fifty Years." AI Magazine 27, no. 4, pp. 87-91.

Morby, Alice. 2017a. "Electric flying taxi by Lilium successfully completes its first voyage." Dezeen (April 21). Available at: https://www.dezeen.com/2017/04/21/electric-flying-taxi-aeroplane-lilium-completes-first-voyage/ (accessed July 21, 2019).

Morby, Alice. 2017b. "Dubai to begin flying world's first passenger drone." Dezeen. (February 14). Available at: https://www.dezeen.com/2017/02/14/dubai-begin-flying-world-first-passenger-drone-transport-technology-news/ (accessed July 27, 2019).

Mozur, Paul. 2018. "Inside China's Dystopian Dreams: A.I., Shame and Lots of Cameras." *The New York Times* (July 8, 2018). Available at: https://www.nytimes.com/2018/07/08/business/china-surveillance-technology.html (accessed May 25, 2019).

Mpetey, Godfrey. 2019. "U.S. Bank, ATA and North@ Work aim to address truck driver shortage." US Bank. Available at: https://www.usbank.com/newsroom/stories/us-bank-ata-and-northatwork-aim-to-address-truck-driver-shortage.html (accessed July 30, 2019).

Munro, Jay. 1998. "Speech Technology Timeline." ZDNet (March 10). Available at: http://www.zdnet.com/pcmag/features/speech/sb1.html (accessed April 12, 2019).

NCSL (National Conference of State Legislatures). 2019. "Autonomous Vehicles | Self-Driving Vehicles Enacted Legislation." NCSL (March 19). Available at: http://www.ncsl.org/research/transportation/autonomous-vehicles-self-driving-vehicles-enacted-legislation.aspx (accessed April 24, 2019).

"A Next Generation Artificial Intelligence Development Plan." 2017. China Copyright and Media (July 20), trans. Graham Webster, et.al. Available at: https://chinacopyrightandmedia.wordpress.com/2017/07/20/a-next-generation-artificial-intelligence-development-plan/ (accessed April 21, 2019).

Nodal Exchange. 2019. *Trucking Freight Futures.* Available at: https://static1.squarespace.com/ static/5899e78b1b10e35238fba886/t/5b63466b-03ce641a49090764/1533232748289/Trucking-Freight -Futures.pdf (accessed July 23, 2019).

Noonan, Laura. 2017. "Deutsche boss calls for 'revolutionary spirit' as robots take jobs." Financial Times (September 6). Available at: https://www.ft.com/ content/398836c4-92e0-11e7-a9e6-11d2f0ebb7f0 (accessed July 21, 2019).

Noor, Nadav et al. 2019. "3D Printing of Personalized Thick and Perfusable Cardiac Patches and Hearts." Advanced Science (April 15). Available at: https://onlinelibrary.wiley.com/doi/full/10.1002/ advs.201900344 (accessed April 14, 2019).

Nordqvist, Christian. 2019. "AI and machine learning at Equifax." Marketbusinessnews (January 19). Available at: https://marketbusinessnews.com/ ai-machine-learning-equifax/194718/, (accessed July 27, 2019).

NVIDIA. 2017. "NVIDIA Paves Path to AI Cities with Metropolis Edge-to-Cloud Platform for Video Analytics." Available at: https://nvidianews.nvidia. com/news/nvidia-paves-path-to-ai-cities-with-metropolis-edge-to-cloud-platform-for-video-analytics (accessed April 11, 2019).

OECD (Organisation for Economic Co-operation and Development). 2018. *Private Equity Investment in Artificial Intelligence.* OECD Going Digital Policy Note. Paris. Available at: www.oecd.org/going-digital/ai/private-equity-investment-in-artificial-intelligence.pdf (accessed April 29, 2019).

Overby, Stephanie. 2017. "Creators: Social Robotics Pioneer Cynthia Breazeal Builds Your BFF." Digitalist Magazine (November 15). Available at: https://www.digitalistmag.com/machine-learning-ai/2017/11/15/creators-social-robotics-pioneer-cynthia-brezeal-builds-your-bff-05486827 (accessed April 30, 2019).

Paikeday, Tony. 2018. "NVIDIA and Baker Hughes, a GE Company, Pump AI Into Oil & Gas Industry." NVIDIA (January 29). Available at: https://blogs.nvidia.com/blog/2018/01/29/baker-hughes-ge-nvidia-ai/ (accessed June 30, 2019).

Pan, Yunhe. 2016. "Heading toward Artificial Intelligence 2.0." Engineering 2, no. 4 (December): pp. 409-413.

Panetta, Kasey. 2018. "5 Trends Emerge in the Gartner Hype Cycle for Emerging Technologies." Gartner (August 16). Available at: https://www.gartner.com/smarterwithgartner/5-trends-emerge-in-gartner-hype-cycle-for-emerging-technologies-2018/ (accessed April 17, 2019).

ParkLee, Eunice et. al. 2017. "Receipt of Services for Substance Use and Mental Health Issues Among Adults: Results from the 2016 National Survey on Drug Use and Health." NSDUH DATA REVIEW (September). Available at: https://www.samhsa.gov/data/sites/default/files/NSDUH-DR-FFR2-2016/NSDUH-DR-FFR2-2016.pdf (accessed April 18, 2019).

Peng, Hanyong et al. 2017. "A microRNA-initiated DNAzyme motor operating in living cells." Nature Communications 8 (March 6). Available at: https://www.nature.com/articles/ncomms14378 (accessed April 24, 2019).

Penn, David. 2018. "Personetics Scores Minority Stake Investment from United Overseas Bank." Finovate (July 23). Available at: https://finovate.com/personetics-scores-minority-stake-investment-from-united-overseas-bank/ (accessed July 11, 2019).

Peters, Adele. 2018. "Having A Heart Attack? This AI Helps Emergency Dispatchers Find Out." Fast Company (January 11). Available at: https://www.fastcompany.com/40515740/having-a-heart-attack-this-ai-helps-emergency-dispatchers-find-out (accessed April 29, 2019)

Pisarenko, Dmitrii. 2019. "Uznaiut po pokhodke. Kak Kitai stroit u sebia tsifrovuiu diktaturu." Ezhedel'nik "Argumenty i fakty" (April 4). Available at: http://www.aif.ru/politics/world/uznayut_po_pohodke_

kak_kitay_stroit_u_sebya_cifrovuyu_diktaturu (accessed April 28, 2019).

"Planning Outline for the Construction of a Social Credit System (2014-2020)." 2014. China Copyright and Media (June 14), ed. Rogier Creemers. Available at: https://chinacopyrightandmedia.wordpress.com/2014/06/14/planning-outline-for-the-construction-of-a-social-credit-system-2014-2020/ (accessed July 15, 2019).

Ponkin, Igor' and Alena Red'kina. 2018. "Iskusstvennyi intellekt s tochki zreniia prava." Vestnik RUDN: Legal Sciences series, 22 no. 1.

"Postanovlenie Pravitel'stva Respubliki Kazakhstan ot 12 dekabria 2017 no. 827 ob utverzhdenii Gosudarstvennoi programmy 'Tsifrovoi Kazakhstan.'" 2017, as July 29, 2019. Available at: https://online.zakon.kz/Document/?doc_id=37168057 (accessed August 20, 2019)

Premack, Rachel. 2018. "Truck driver salaries have fallen by as much as 50% since the 1970s—and experts say a little-known law explains why." Business Insider (September 26). Available at: https://www.businessinsider.com/truck-driver-salary-decrease-pay-cut-2018-9 (accessed July 8, 2019).

Priyanka, Roy. 2018. "Intelligent automation could add $512 billion to the global revenues of financial services firms by 2020." Capgemini. Available at: https://www.capgemini.com/no-no/news/intelligent-automation-could-add-512-billion-to-the-global-revenues-of-financial-services-firms-by-2020/ (accessed July 21, 2019).

PWC (PricewaterhouseCoopers). 2017. "Sizing the prize: What's the real value of AI for your business and how can you capitalise?" Available at: https://www.pwc.com/gx/en/issues/analytics/assets/pwc-ai-analysis-sizing-the-prize-report.pdf (accessed April 24, 2019).

PWC (PricewaterhouseCoopers). 2018a. "US$320 billion by 2030? The potential impact of AI in the Middle East." Available at: https://www.pwc.com/m1/en/publications/documents/economic-potential-ai-middle-east.pdf (accessed July 6, 2019).

PWC (PricewaterhouseCoopers). 2018b. *Pulling fraud out of the shadows*. Global Economic Crime and Fraud Survey 2018. Available at: https://www.pwc.com/gx/en/forensics/global-economic-crime-and-fraud-survey-2018.pdf (accessed July 19, 2019).

Rapier, Graham. 2018. "Waymo is worth $100 billion more than previous estimates, Morgan Stanley says (GOOGL)." MarketInsider (August 7). Available at: https://markets.businessinsider.com/news/stocks/google-stock-price-waymo-worth-100-billion-more-than-before-morgan-stanley-2018-8-1027439248?utm_source=markets&utm_medium=ingest (accessed April 17, 2019).

Ravenscroft, Tom. 2019. "Lyons Place by Farrells set to be London's first housing to accept drone deliveries." Dezeen (February 14). Available at: https://www.dezeen.com/2019/02/14/drone-deliveries-lyons-place-farrells-london/ (accessed July 6, 2019).

"Razvitie iskusstvennogo intellekta v stranakh mira: SShA, Kitai, Velikobritaniia." 2019. D-russia (April 10). Available at: http://d-russia.ru/razvitie-iskusstvennogo-intellekta-v-stranah-mira-ssha-kitaj-velikobritaniya.html (accessed April 12, 2019).

Reddy, Raj. 1996. "The challenge of artificial intelligence." Computer 29 no. 10, (October): 92. Available at: https://www.ri.cmu.edu/pub_files/pub2/reddy_raj_1996_1/reddy_raj_1996_1.pdf (accessed April 17, 2019).

Roberts, David. 2017. "A fascinating new scheme to create walkable public spaces in Barcelona." Vox (April 22). Available at: https://www.vox.com/2016/8/4/12342806/barcelona-superblocks (accessed July 14, 2019).

"Robot nachal rabotat' v kontakt-tsentre korporativnykh klientov Sberbanka." 2018. Banki.ru News Agency (February 26). Available at: https://www.banki.ru/news/lenta/?id=10300539 (accessed July 9, 2019).

Roehrig, Charles. 2016. "Mental Disorders Top the List of the Most Costly Conditions in the United States:

$201 Billion." HealthAffairs 35, no.6, (June). Available at: https://www.healthaffairs.org/doi/full/10.1377/hlthaff.2015.1659#EX1(accessed July 11, 2019).

"Rolls-Royce and Finferries Demonstrate World's First Fully Autonomous Ferry." 2018. MI News Network (December 4). Available at: https://www.marineinsight.com/shipping-news/rolls-royce-and-finferries-demonstrate-worlds-first-fully-autonomous-ferry/ (accessed July 9, 2019).

Rosenberg, Louis. 2017. "New Hope for Humans in an AI World." TEDxKC. Available at: https://www.youtube.com/watch?v=Eu-RyZt_Uas (accessed April 17, 2019).

Scherer, Matthew U. 2016. "Regulating Artificial Intelligence Systems: Risks, Challenges, Competencies, and Strategies." Harvard Journal of Law & Technology 29, no. 2. Available at: https://papers.ssrn.com/sol3/papers.cfm?abstract_id=2609777 (accessed April 11, 2019).

Schlecht, Daniel et. al. 2017. "Artificial Intelligence: The Ultimate Disrupting Force for Oil and Gas Companies." The First SPE Norway Magazine 3, (September): 8-11. Available at: https://higherlogicdownload.s3.amazonaws.com/SPE/a9890ca7-fae3-4ee2-8ea9-4dc3623a372a/UploadedImages/Oslo%20Magazine/TheFirst_September_2017-vol3-resized1.pdf (accessed July 28, 2019).

Schroerlucke, Samuel R. et al. 2017. "Complication Rate in Robotic-Guided vs Fluoro-Guided Minimally Invasive Spinal Fusion Surgery: Report from MIS Refresh Prospective Comparative Study." The Spine Journal 17, no. 10 (October): 254-255.

Shahi, Gurinder S. and Eng Fong Pang (editors). 2009. *Technology in a Changing World.* GBI Books.

Shead, Sam. 2018. "Baidu Leads AI Patent Applications In China With 2,368 Filings." Forbes (December 4). Available at: https://www.forbes.com/sites/samshead/2018/12/04/baidu-leads-ai-patent-applications-in-china-with-2368-filings/#4257decb28ae (accessed July 16, 2019).

Si, Ma. 2018. "Microsoft expands presence of AI platform Xiaoice." China Daily (July 28). Available at: http://www.chinadaily.com.cn/a/201807/28/WS5b-5baf5ea31031a351e90b14.html (accessed July 4, 2019).

Sipherd, Ray. 2018. "The third-leading cause of death in US most doctors don't want you to know about." CNBC (February 22). Available at: https://www.cnbc.com/2018/02/22/medical-errors-third-leading-cause-of-death-in-america.html (accessed April 14, 2019).

Smith, Chris, et.al. 2006. "The history of Artificial Intelligence" (course paper). Available at: https://courses.cs.washington.edu/courses/csep590/06au/projects/history-ai.pdf (accessed August 13, 2019).

Soo, Zen. 2018. "Microsoft's AI bot writes poetry, hosts a TV show and can converse like a human in Mandarin." South China Morning Post. (May 23). Available at: https://www.scmp.com/tech/enterprises/article/2147373/microsofts-ai-bot-writes-poetry-hosts-tv-show-and-can-converse (accessed July 23, 2019).

"SparkCognition Adds Artificial Intelligence to Aker BP's Operations." 2019. PR Newswire (March 26). Available at: https://www.prnewswire.com/news-releases/sparkcognition-adds-artificial-intelligence-to-aker-bps-operations-300818227.html (accessed July 6, 2019).

Spencer, Geoff. 2018. "Much more than a chatbot: China's Xiaoice mixes AI with emotions and wins over millions of fans." NEWS.MICROSOFT.COM (November 1). Available at: https://news.microsoft.com/apac/features/much-more-than-a-chatbot-chinas-xiaoice-mixes-ai-with-emotions-and-wins-over-millions-of-fans/ (accessed July 5, 2019).

"SShA vnesli Huawei v chernyi spisok iz-za ugrozy natsional'noi bezopasnosti." 2019. BBC News Russian Service (May 16). Available at: https://www.bbc.com/russian/news-48290283 (accessed May 30, 2019).

Steadman, Ian. 2013. "IBM's Watson is better at diagnosing cancer than human doctors." Wired Magazine UK (February 11). Available at: https://www.

wired.co.uk/article/ibm-watson-medical-doctor (accessed June 10, 2019).

Stilgoe, Jack. 2019. "Who killed Elaine Herzberg? One year on from the Uber crash." Driverless Futures (May 18). Available at: https://driverless-futures. com/2019/03/18/who-killed-elaine-herzberg-one-year-on-from-the-uber-crash/ (accessed April 11, 2019).

"Swedish bank Nordea to introduce artificial intelligence." 2017. FinTech Bulletin (July 21). Available at: http://bulletins.bfconsulting.com/en/swedish-bank-nordea-to-introduce-artificial-intelligence/ (accessed July 13, 2019).

Swilling, Mark et al. 2013. "City-Level Decoupling." UNEP International Resource Panel. Available at: https://www.resourcepanel.org/reports/city-level-decoupling (accessed July 25, 2019).

Takahashi, Motoki. 2018. "AI trounces humans in forex forecasting debut." NIKKEI Asian Review (February 1). Available at: https://asia.nikkei.com/ Business/Markets/Currencies/AI-trounces-humans-in-forex-forecasting-debut (accessed July 13, 2019).

Tate, Karl. 2014. "History of A.I.: Artificial Intelligence." Live Science (August 25). Available at: https:// www.livescience.com/47544-history-of-a-i-artificial-intelligence-infographic.html (accessed April 15, 2019).

Tham, Irene. 2019. "Immediate need for locals to plug ai talent gap in s'pore, says Israeli expert." Straits Times (March 29). Available at: https://www.a-star. edu.sg/News-and-Events/A-STAR-INNOVATE/Index/ ID/7917 (accessed April 19, 2019).

Thierer, Adam and Andrea Castillo. 2016. "Preparing for the Future of Artificial Intelligence." Public Interest Comment to the Office of Science and Technology Policy (April 24). Available at: https://www. mercatus.org/system/files/Thierer-Artificial-Intelligence-Permissionless-Innovation-PIC-v1.pdf (accessed April 8, 2019).

"Think 2019 Kicks Off with Live Debate between Man and Machine." 2019. New York: IBM. Available at: https://www.ibm.com/blogs/research/2019/02/ai-debate-recap-think-2019/ (accessed April 10, 2019).

"Total to Develop Artificial Intelligence Solutions with Google Cloud." 2018. Available at: https://www. total.com/en/media/news/press-releases/total-develop-artificial-intelligence-solutions-google-cloud (accessed June 20, 2019).

Turing, Alan. 1950. "Computing Machinery and Intelligence." Mind, no. 236 (October): pp. 433-460.

Ungarino, Rebecca. 2018. "Waymo could be a $250 billion win for Alphabet, Jefferies says (GOOGL)." MarketInsider (December 19). Available at: https://markets.businessinsider.com/news/stocks/alphabet-stock-waymo-could-be-a-250-billion-deal-jefferies-says-2018-12-1027823079 (accessed April 8, 2019).

United Nations. 2018. "68% of the world population projected to live in urban areas by 2050." UN news (May 16). Available at: https://www.un.org/development/desa/en/news/population/2018-revision-of-world-urbanization-prospects.html (accessed April 8, 2019).

University of Tokyo. 2019. "New nanomedicine slips through the cracks, reaches brain: Nanomachines aim to deliver cancer drugs to hard-to-reach areas like the brain." Reported by ScienceDaily (April 24). Available at: www.sciencedaily.com/releases/2019/04/190424083400.htm (accessed April 14, 2019).

Valeriani, Davide. 2017. "Elon Musk wants to merge man and machine—here's what he'll need to work out." The Conversation (April 1). Available at: https://theconversation.com/elon-musk-wants-to-merge-man-and-machine-heres-what-hell-need-to-work-out-75321 (accessed April 22, 2019).

Vinge, Vernor. 2013. "The Coming Technological Singularity: How to Survive in the Post-Human Era." Prepared for VISION-21 Symposium, sponsored by

NASA Lewis Research Center and the Ohio Aerospace Institute, March 30-31, 1993. Available at: https://edoras.sdsu.edu/~vinge/misc/singularity.html (accessed August 14, 2019).

Walker, Jon. 2019. "The Self-Driving Car Timeline—Predictions from the Top 11 Global Automakers." Emerj (May 14). Available at: https://emerj.com/ai-adoption-timelines/self-driving-car-timeline-themselves-top-11-automakers/ (accessed May 26, 2019).

Watanabe, Simiyo et al. 2019. "In vivo rendezvous of small nucleic acid drugs with charge-matched block catiomers to target cancers." Nature Communications 10, Article number: 1894. Available at: https://www.nature.com/articles/s41467-019-09856-w (accessed May 17, 2019).

WHO (World Health Organization). 2016. Global Report On Diabetes. Available at: https://apps.who.int/iris/bitstream/handle/10665/204871/9789241565257_eng.pdf;jsessionid=7A6138D92636F1DA2941EE5FA-3F3A1AD?sequence=1(accessed April 11, 2019).

WHO (World Health Organization). 2017. World Health Rankings. Available at: https://www.worldlifeexpectancy.com/cause-of-death/road-traffic-accidents/by-country/ (accessed April 9, 2019).

WHO (World Health Organization). 2018. Global status report on road safety 2018: World Health Organization summary. Geneva. Available at: https://www.

who.int/violence_injury_prevention/road_safety_sta-tus/2018/English-Summary-GSRRS2018.pdf (accessed April 25, 2019).

Wooldridge, Michael. 2018. *Artificial Intelligence: Everything you need to know about the coming AI.* London: Penguin Random House.

"ZestFinance Receives Funding from Baidu to Fuel Development of Search-Based Under-writing Technology." 2016. BusinessWire (July 18). Available at: https://www.businesswire.com/news/home/20160717005040/en/ZestFi-nance-Receives-Funding-Baidu-Fuel-Develop-ment-Search-Based (accessed July 17, 2019).

Notes

[1] The OED defines "big data" as "Data of a very large size, typically to the extent that its manipulation and management present significant logistical challenges; (also) the branch of computing involving such data." See http://www.oed.com/view/Entry/18833#eid301162177 (accessed April 10, 2019).

[2] "Metropolis" is a silent 2.5-hour feature film by Fritz Lang based on the script and parallel to the novel by Thea von Harbou, an epic metaphorical and science fiction dystopia.

[3] Vannevar Bush was an American scientist, engineer, developer of analog computers, methodologist and organizer of scientific research and the scientific community. He served as science advisor to President Franklin Delano Roosevelt.

[4] Alan Turing was an English mathematician, logician, cryptographer, who had a significant impact on the development of computer science. The abstract computing "Turing Machine" proposed by him in 1936 made it possible to formalize the concept of an algorithm and is still used in many theoretical and practical studies. Turing's scientific works are a universally recognized contribution to the foundations of computer science and, in particular, to the theory of artificial intelligence.

[5] John McCarthy was an American computer scientist, the author of the term "artificial intelligence," the inventor of the Lisp computer language, and a Turing Award winner for his enormous contribution to the field of artificial intelligence research.

[6] RAND is an American nonprofit organization, a strategic research center commissioned by the US government and the armed forces, as well as related organizations.

[7] Herbert A. Simon was an American scientist in the field of social, political and economic sciences, winner of the Nobel Prize in Economics (1978) and the Turing Award (1975). His work in the field of computer technology and artificial intelligence had a significant impact on the development of cybernetics.

[8] ELIZA is a virtual interlocutor, the famous computer program written by Joseph Weizenbaum in 1966, which mimics dialogue with a therapist using the technique of active listening.

[9] PARRY is a program developed by psychiatrist Kenneth Colby that simulates human behavior with paranoid schizophrenia and also simulated a conversational strategy.

[10] DARPA (the Defense Advanced Research Projects Agency) is an agency of the United States Department of Defense responsible for the development of emerging technologies for use by the military.

¹¹ Boston Dynamics is an American engineering company specializing in robotics; its parent company is SoftBank Group. See: https://www.bostondynamics.com/

¹² Hanson Robotics Limited is a Hong Kong-based robotics engineering company founded by David Hanson, known for its development of human-like robots. See: https://www.hansonrobotics.com/

¹³ Reddy was awarded the Turing Prize in 1994 for his achievements in the study of artificial intelligence.

¹⁴ Jürgen Schmidhuber is the founder and chief researcher of NNAISENSE, and director of the Swiss AI lab IDSIA.

¹⁵ Patrick Winston is a well-known computer scientist, the former director of the MIT Computer Science and Artificial Intelligence Laboratory.

¹⁶ Louis Rosenberg is CEO of Unanimous AI.

¹⁷ See also: https://www.cfr.org/event/future-artificial-intelligence-and-its-impact-society

¹⁸ See: https://news.itu.int/the-future-is-better-than-you-think-predictions-on-ai-and-development-from-ray-kurzweil/

¹⁹ See: https://www.arterys.com/

[20] See: https://www.viz.ai/

[21] See: https://www.zebra-med.com/solutions/

[22] See: https://paige.ai/

[23] See: https://www.butterflynetwork.com/

[24] See: https://www.eyediagnosis.net/

[25] See: http://www.euro.who.int/en/health-topics/noncommunicable-diseases/diabetes/data-and-statistics

[26] See: https://www.atomwise.com/

[27] See: https://www.iapb.org/vision-2020/who-facts/

[28] See: https://nfb.org/resources/blindness-statistics

[29] See: https://www.qventus.com/

[30] See: https://alice.yandex.ru/help

[31] See: https://alice.yandex.ru/smart-home#video_top

[32] See: http://en.people.cn/n3/2017/0531/c90000-9222463.html

33 See: https://www.sberbank.ru/ru/press_center/all/article?newsID=d268f1d0-5422-44cd-98f1-b79c95734628&blockID=1303&regionID=77&lang=ru

34 See: https://www.lenddo.com/

35 See: https://www.zestfinance.com/

36 See: https://www.upstart.com/

37 See: https://newsroom.bankofamerica.com/press-releases/consumer-banking/bank-americas-ericar-surpasses-6-million-users

38 See: https://www.ocbc.com/group/media/release/2017/home-and-renovation-loan-specialist-ai-emma.html

39 See: https://www.bnymellon.com/us/en/newsroom/news/press-releases/bny-mellons-automation-efforts-draw-industry-accolades.jsp

40 See: https://www.db.com/newsroom_news/2017/deutsche-bank-rolls-out-new-ai-based-equities-algorithmic-platform-in-apac-en-11748.htm

41 See: https://newsroom.mastercard.com/press-releases/mastercard-rolls-out-artificial-intelligence-across-its-global-network/

[42] See: https://www.sberbank.kz/ru/press_center/category/novosti/post/2177-kak-iskusstvennyj-intellekt-stoit-na-strazhe-vashih-fi

[43] See: https://www.kount.com/

[44] See: https://www.sas.com/en_us/software/credit-scoring-for-enterprise-miner.html

[45] See a summary of the report "Autonomous Vehicles Market 2019–2024" at https://www.researchandmarkets.com/research/mc83t6/autonomous?w=12 (accessed July 18, 2019).

[46] See: https://www.forbes.com/global2000/list/#-header:marketValue_sortreverse:true

[47] See: https://www.trucking.org/News_and_Information_Reports.aspx

[48] See: http://www.ehang.com/ehang184/index

[49] See: https://www.nhtsa.gov/technology-innovation/vehicle-vehicle-communication

[50] See: https://www.oodihelsinki.fi/en/

[51] See: https://www.sidewalklabs.com

[52] See: http://opendata.cityofnewyork.us/

[53] RFID (Radio Frequency Identification) is a contactless data exchange technology based on the use of radio frequency electromagnetic radiation.

[54] USN (Ubiquitous Sensor Networks) are networks that connect all possible sensors in a given environment.

[55] LEED (Leadership in Energy and Environmental Design) is a set of energy and environmental design guidelines, a voluntary green building certification system developed in 1998 by the American Green Building Council to evaluate energy efficiency and sustainability of sustainable development projects.

[56] See: https://ndr.ogauthority.co.uk/dp/controller/

[57] See: https://www.gazprom-neft.ru/press-center/lib/1993667/

[58] See: https://www.gazprom-neft.ru/press-center/news/3033857/

[59] See: http://www.gov.cn/zhengce/content/2014-06/27/content_8913.htm

[60] See: https://www.internetlivestats.com/google-search-statistics/?office=3535

[61] See: https://www.Facebook.com/pg/Facebook/about/

62 See: https://www.statista.com/statistics/264810/number-of-monthly-active-Facebook-users-worldwide/

63 See: https://www.statista.com/statistics/253577/number-of-monthly-active-instagram-users/

64 See: https://www.statista.com/statistics/730306/whatsapp-status-dau/

65 See: https://www.huawei.com/en/

66 See: https://www.cnbc.com/video/2019/06/21/watch-cnbcs-full-interview-with-huawei-founder-and-ceo-ren-zhengfei.html

67 See: http://www.tencent.com/en-us/index.html

68 See: https://www.alibabagroup.com/en/global/home

69 See: https://cnnic.com.cn/

70 See: https://www.statista.com/statistics/467160/forecast-of-smartphone-users-in-china/

71 See: https://www.whitehouse.gov/presidential-actions/executive-order-maintaining-american-leadership-artificial-intelligence/

72 See: https://www.nrf.gov.sg/programmes/artificial-intelligence-r-d-programme

73 Mekhanik, Aleksandr. "'Ochen' zhelatel'no Vashe prisutstvie.'" Published on Stimul. Available at: https://stimul.online/historical-dates/ochen-zhe-latelno-vashe-prisutstvie/ (accessed August 20, 2019).

74 See:https://stoddart.northwestern.edu/fraser-stoddart/

75 See: https://www.nobelprize.org/prizes/chemis-try/2016/press-release/

76 See: https://futureoflife.org/ai-principles/

77 "Runaround" was written by Asimov in October 1941 and first published in March 1942 in Astounding Science Fiction.

78 See: https://informburo.kz/novosti/nursul-tan-nazarbaev-vystupaet-s-ezhegodnym-posla-niem-narodu-kazahstana.html

79 See: https://egov.kz/cms/ru/information/about/stat

80 See: https://digitalkz.kz/cifrovizaciya-otraslei-economiki/

81 See: https://digitalkz.kz/cifrovizaciya-otraslei-economiki/